STARS® SERIES
C

STRATEGIES TO ACHIEVE READING SUCCESS

- ☐ PROVIDES INSTRUCTIONAL ACTIVITIES FOR 12 READING STRATEGIES
- ☐ USES A STEP-BY-STEP APPROACH TO ACHIEVE READING SUCCESS
- ☐ PREPARES STUDENTS FOR ASSESSMENT IN READING COMPREHENSION

CURRICULUM ASSOCIATES®, INC.

ACKNOWLEDGMENTS

Product Development

Developers and Writers: Deborah Adcock and Joan Krensky
Contributing Writer: Patricia Delanie
Editor: Deborah Adcock

Design and Production

Designer: Jamie Ruh
Cover Design: Christine Gilbert

Illustration Credits

Susan Hawk/pages 50, 52, 65, 76, 79, 84, 99, 104, 129, 130, 135, 140
Jamie Ruh/pages 6, 10, 12, 18, 21, 23, 26, 28, 31, 40, 42, 67, 74

Photography Credits

Jamie Ruh/pages 45, 68
www.arttoday.com/pages 16, 23, 94, 120
Courtesy of Children's Defense Fund, Washington, D.C./page 102
Courtesy of Federation Internationale de Football Association, Zurich, Switzerland/page 123
Library of Congress, Prints and Photographs Division, LC-USZ62-119882/page 33

ISBN 978-0-7609-3585-9

North Billerica, MA 01862

15 14 13 12 11 10 9 8 7 6 5

TABLE OF CONTENTS

Strategy One FINDING MAIN IDEA

PART ONE: Think About Main Idea

WHAT IS MAIN IDEA?

Stories, poems, and articles all have a main idea. A movie or television show also has a main idea. The main idea tells what something is mostly about.

★ Write the name of a book you have read in school or at home.

____

____

★ Write some of the things that happen in the book.

____

____

____

★ Tell what the book is mostly about.

____

____

____

You just wrote about main idea!

Tell your partner about a movie you have seen or a TV show you have watched. Then take turns telling the main idea of the movie or TV show. Try to tell your main idea in one sentence.

How Do You Find the Main Idea?

You can find the main idea of most reading passages in the first sentence or in the last sentence of the passage. Read the passage below.

> Dolphins are small, toothed whales that live in the ocean. Dolphins are mammals. They live in groups called pods. There are more than thirty different kinds of dolphins.

Think about the most important idea in the passage.

Let's find the main idea.

Look at the triangle below. The first three sentences tell about the main idea, but they do not tell the most important idea.

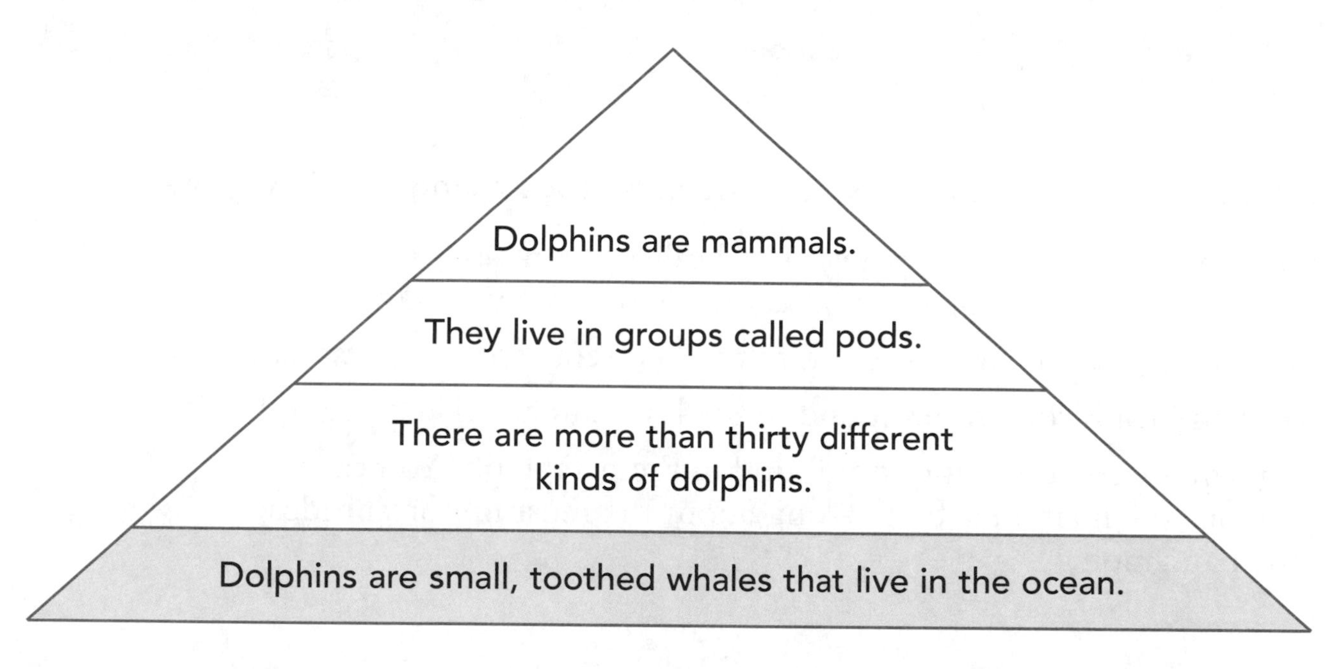

The sentence at the bottom of the triangle is the most important idea. This sentence tells what the passage is mostly about. The main idea is found in the first sentence of the passage.

> You just found the main idea!

Read what Louis wrote about frogs. As you read, think about the most important idea in the paragraph.

Frogs change as they grow. Frogs begin as eggs. A frog egg looks like a tiny black dot in jelly. In time, a frog egg changes into a tadpole. A tadpole has a tail. It breathes underwater and has gills like a fish. Later, the tadpole develops legs, and its tail gets shorter. It grows lungs to replace its gills. The tadpole is now a frog that can live on land.

egg → tadpole → frog

The most important idea in Louis's paragraph is **Frogs change as they grow.**

The most important idea in a paragraph is called the **main idea.**
The main idea tells what a paragraph is mostly or mainly about.

★ The main idea is sometimes found in the first sentence of a paragraph.

★ The main idea is sometimes found in the last sentence of a paragraph.

★ The main idea is sometimes not found in the paragraph. You can figure out the main idea by thinking about the most important idea in the paragraph.

Read this paragraph about Ben. As you read, think about the main idea of the paragraph. Then answer the questions.

Sick Day

Ben picked up a book and started to read. After a few minutes, he closed the book with a sigh. Then he turned on the television. Ben flipped through a dozen channels, but he couldn't find anything he wanted to watch. His lunch sat on the table by his bed. He wasn't even hungry. Ben had to admit that staying home sick can be boring.

1. What is the main idea of the paragraph?

Ⓐ Ben doesn't feel like eating.

Ⓑ Ben likes to read when he is sick.

Ⓒ Staying home sick can be boring.

Ⓓ There is nothing on television during the day.

2. Where or how did you find the main idea?

Ⓐ in the first sentence of the paragraph

Ⓑ in the last sentence of the paragraph

Ⓒ in the middle of the paragraph

Ⓓ by thinking about the most important idea in the paragraph

Talk about your answers to questions 1 and 2.
Tell why you chose the answers you did.

PART THREE: Check Your Understanding

Remember: The main idea tells what a paragraph is mostly or mainly about.

★ Read the first sentence of the paragraph. The main idea is sometimes found here.

★ Read the last sentence of the paragraph. The main idea is sometimes found here.

★ Sometimes, the main idea is not found in a sentence from the paragraph. You can figure out the main idea by thinking about the most important idea in the paragraph.

Read this article about celebrations. As you read, ask yourself, "What is the article mostly about?" Then answer the questions.

When do you celebrate the new year? In the United States, Europe, and Japan, most people celebrate the new year on January 1. In China, the new year begins sometime between the middle of February and the middle of March. Jewish people celebrate the Jewish new year in the fall. In Iran, the new year begins on the first day of spring.

3. What is the article mostly about?

Ⓐ countries that celebrate the new year on January 1

Ⓑ why the new year begins on a different day each year

Ⓒ different times that the new year is celebrated

Ⓓ people who begin the new year in the fall

4. Where or how did you find the main idea?

Ⓐ in the first sentence of the paragraph

Ⓑ in the last sentence of the paragraph

Ⓒ in the middle of the paragraph

Ⓓ by thinking about the most important idea in the paragraph

Look at the answer choices for each question. Read why each answer choice is correct or not correct.

3. What is the article mostly about?

Ⓐ countries that celebrate the new year on January 1

This answer is not correct because the article tells about many countries that celebrate the new year on different days.

Ⓑ why the new year begins on a different day each year

This answer is not correct because the new year is not on a different day each year. Different people celebrate the new year on different days.

● different times that the new year is celebrated

This answer is correct because it is the most important idea. It tells what the article is mostly about.

Ⓓ people who begin the new year in the fall

This answer is not correct because it is not the most important idea of the article. This answer does not tell what the article is mostly about.

4. Where or how did you find the main idea?

Ⓐ in the first sentence of the paragraph

This answer is not correct because the first sentence is "When do you celebrate the new year?" *This is not the most important idea in the article.*

Ⓑ in the last sentence of the paragraph

This answer is not correct because the last sentence is "In Iran, the new year begins on the first day of spring." *This is not the most important idea in the article.*

Ⓒ in the middle of the paragraph

This answer is not correct because the middle of the paragraph tells about when people in China celebrate the new year. Also, the main idea is more often found in the first or last sentence of a paragraph, not in the middle of a paragraph.

● by thinking about the most important idea in the paragraph

This answer is correct because the main idea is not found in the first sentence, the last sentence, or in the middle of a paragraph. The main idea is found by thinking about the most important idea in the article. This answer tells about all the other ideas in the article.

PART FOUR: Learn More About Main Idea

★ Each paragraph in a reading passage has one main idea. The whole reading passage also has one main idea. The main idea of a whole reading passage is often found in the first or last paragraph.

★ The title of a reading passage tells something about the main idea.

Read this article about birds. Then answer the questions.

Outside and Inside

Birds have two kinds of feathers. The outside feathers help keep the bird dry. These feathers cover each other. They form a kind of raincoat for the bird. These outside feathers are flat and smooth.

Under these outside feathers is a different kind of feather. These feathers are called "down." Down feathers are soft and fluffy. Down feathers are right next to the bird's skin. The down keeps the bird warm. Baby birds have only down feathers. As they get bigger, their outer feathers grow in.

5. What is the main idea of the first paragraph?

Ⓐ Outside feathers are flat and smooth.
Ⓑ Outside feathers keep birds dry.
Ⓒ Feathers keep a bird dry.
Ⓓ Birds have feathers.

6. What is the main idea of the last paragraph?

Ⓐ Down feathers keep birds warm.
Ⓑ Down feathers are fluffy.
Ⓒ Feathers keep birds warm.
Ⓓ Baby birds have only down feathers.

7. What is the article mostly about?

Ⓐ As birds get bigger, their outer feathers grow in.
Ⓑ Birds have two kinds of feathers.
Ⓒ All birds have feathers.
Ⓓ Feathers are called "down."

8. What is another good title for this article?

Ⓐ "Baby Birds"
Ⓑ "Where to Find Birds"
Ⓒ "How Birds Fly"
Ⓓ "All About Feathers"

Read this story about Tyna. Then answer the questions.

Tyna rushed into the house and called for her mother. She couldn't wait to describe her first day at camp.

"Camp was great," said Tyna. "I met a lot of kids, and we had fun together swimming, playing basketball, and painting."

"I met one boy who's from California. He's here visiting his grandmother. His mother is a doctor. He's an only child, so he gets lonely sometimes. He's going into third grade, like me. We have lots in common, too. He likes tennis and lizards and collects stamps."

"And what's this boy's name?" asked Mother.

"How would I know?" said Tyna, surprised by her mother's question. "Kids don't talk about personal stuff, Mom." Tyna's mom chuckled as Tyna went outside to play with her neighborhood friends.

9. What is the main idea of paragraph 2?

Ⓐ Tyna did not want to go to camp.
Ⓑ Tyna had fun swimming at camp.
Ⓒ Tyna had had a good day at camp.
Ⓓ Tyna looked for her mother.

10. What is the main idea of paragraph 3?

Ⓐ Tyna met a new friend.
Ⓑ Tyna had fun swimming.
Ⓒ Tyna enjoyed her day.
Ⓓ Tyna had trouble making new friends.

11. The story is mostly about

Ⓐ how to make new friends.
Ⓑ playing sports.
Ⓒ a first day at camp.
Ⓓ things people do at camp.

12. What is a good title for this story?

Ⓐ "Trouble at Camp"
Ⓑ "Boy from California"
Ⓒ "Fun at Camp"
Ⓓ "Tyna's New Friend"

PART FIVE: Prepare for a Test

★ A test question about the main idea may ask you what a reading passage is *mostly* or *mainly* about.

★ A test question about the main idea may ask you to choose the best title for a reading passage. A good title tells something about the main idea of the whole reading passage.

Read this article about a famous house. Then answer questions about the article. Choose the best answer for Numbers 13 and 14.

The White House is the most famous home in the United States. It is where the President and his family live.

The President's home was not always called the White House. At different times, it was called the President's Mansion, the President's Palace, and the President's House.

The President's House was burned by the British in 1812. Workers painted it bright white to cover the black walls. Soon, people began to call the building the White House. The name stuck. In time, the name was officially changed to the White House.

Finding Main Idea

13. The article is mostly about

Ⓐ where the president lives.

Ⓑ how the White House got its name.

Ⓒ when the White House was burned.

Ⓓ who painted the White House.

Finding Main Idea

14. What is the best title for the article?

Ⓐ "Famous Homes"

Ⓑ "The President's Mansion"

Ⓒ "One Famous House, Many Names"

Ⓓ "Mansions and Palaces"

Read this fable about an ant and a grasshopper. Then answer questions about the fable. Choose the best answer for Numbers 15 and 16.

The Ant and the Grasshopper

One summer day, Grasshopper hopped about, chirping and singing to his heart's content. Ant passed by, carrying a kernel of corn he was taking to his nest.

"Why do you work so hard?" asked Grasshopper. "Come and chat with me."

"I am storing food for the winter," said Ant. "You should do the same."

"Why bother about winter?" said Grasshopper. "We have plenty of food right now." But Ant went on his way and continued his work.

Grasshopper continued being lazy. When the winter came, he had no food. He saw the ants sharing corn and grain every day from the food they had collected in the summer. Then Grasshopper knew: *Prepare today for the things you need tomorrow.*

Finding Main Idea

15. The fable is mostly about

Ⓐ busy ants.
Ⓑ a hungry grasshopper.
Ⓒ planning for the winter.
Ⓓ sharing with others.

Finding Main Idea

16. Another good title for the fable is

Ⓐ "Plan for Tomorrow."
Ⓑ "Take Time to Chirp and Sing."
Ⓒ "Hard Work Can Be Fun."
Ⓓ "Helpful Neighbors."

Strategy Two RECALLING FACTS AND DETAILS

PART ONE: Think About Facts and Details

What Are Facts and Details?

Everything you read has facts and details. Shows you watch on TV or movies you see at the theater also have facts and details. Facts and details tell more about the main idea.

★ Write the main idea of a TV show you watched in the past few days.

____

____

____

★ Write three important things that happened in the TV show.

____

____

____

____

____

You just wrote about facts and details!

Tell your partner about a story you read or your favorite movie. Take turns telling about the main character in the story or movie. Tell all the facts and details that describe this character. When you are done, choose one word that best describes the character.

How Do You Find Facts and Details?

You can find the facts and details in a reading passage by thinking about the main idea. Once you know the main idea, you can find the details that tell more about the main idea. Read the passage below.

> Early pioneers had to build their own homes. They had to catch or grow all of their food. They often became ill with deadly diseases. Early pioneers had difficult lives.

Find the main idea of the passage. It is found in the last sentence.

Let's find the details that tell more about the main idea.

Look at the circle below. The circle tells the main idea.

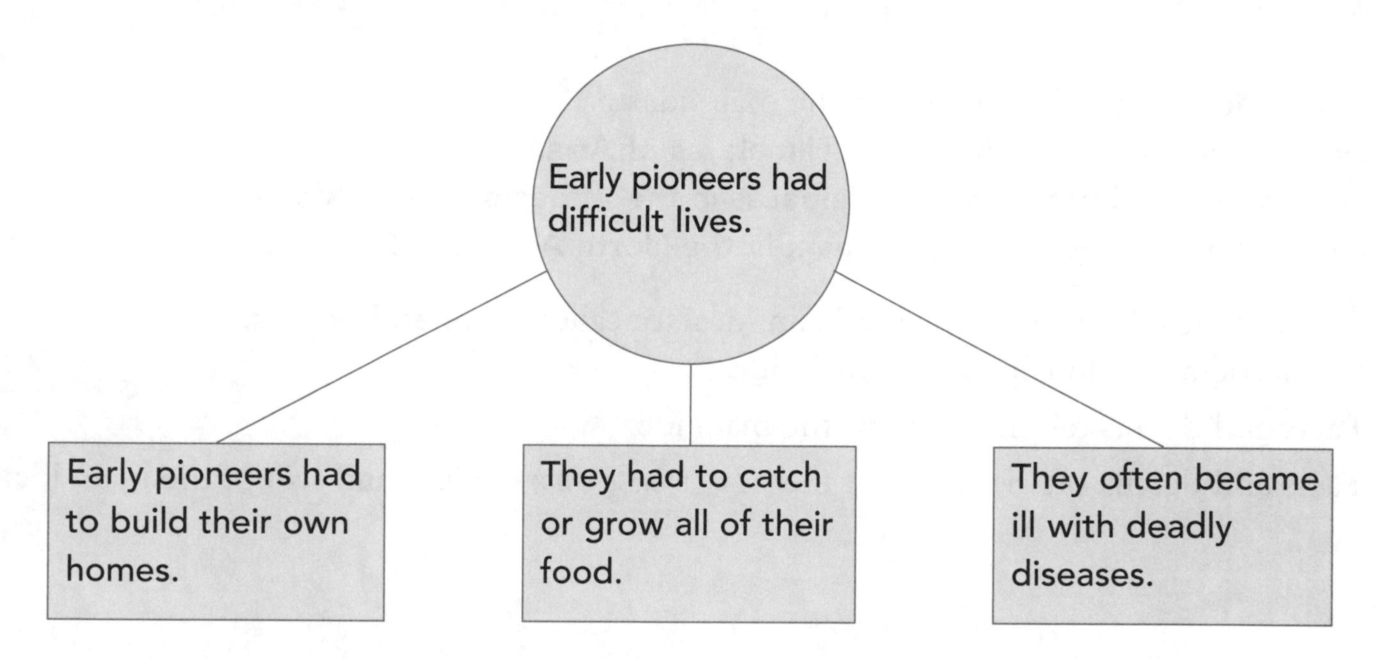

Now look at the rectangles. The rectangles tell more about the main idea. They show the facts and details that help explain the main idea.

> You just found facts and details!

PART TWO: Learn About Facts and Details

Read this paragraph about animals. The main idea is found in the first sentence. It is underlined for you. As you read, think about the sentences that tell more about the main idea.

<u>Many different kinds of animals live on mountains</u>. Snow leopards and yaks live in the Himalayas of Asia. Mountain people herd llamas and alpacas in the Andes of South America. Mountain lions and grizzly bears roam in the North American Rockies.

The sentences that tell more about the main idea are
Snow leopards and yaks live in the Himalayas of Asia.
Mountain people herd llamas and alpacas in the Andes of South America.
Mountain lions and grizzly bears roam in the North American Rockies.

Sentences that tell more about the main idea are called **facts and details.** Facts and details help explain the main idea.

★ Facts and details tell more about the main idea.

★ Facts and details often tell about the *who, what, where, when,* and *why* of the main idea.

Read this story about Tia. The main idea is found in the last sentence. It is underlined for you. As you read, think about the facts and details that tell more about the main idea. Then answer the questions.

Tia lives in California. Her mother is going out of town. Tia will visit her cousin Tomás in New York while her mother is away. Tia has never been to New York. She has never even been on an airplane. Tia is excited about taking her first airplane ride.

1. Who lives in New York?
   - Ⓐ Tia
   - Ⓑ Tia's grandfather
   - Ⓒ Tia's cousin
   - Ⓓ Tia's mother

2. Which detail tells why Tia is going to New York?
   - Ⓐ She has never even been on an airplane.
   - Ⓑ Her mother is going out of town.
   - Ⓒ Tia has never been to New York.
   - Ⓓ Tia lives in California.

Talk about your answers to questions 1 and 2. Tell why you chose the answers you did.

PART THREE: Check Your Understanding

Remember: Facts and details explain the main idea.

★ Look for sentences that tell more about the main idea.

★ Look for sentences that tell about the *who, what, where, when,* and *why* of the main idea.

Read this part of the story that tells more about Tia. As you read, ask yourself, "What is the main idea? What information tells *more* about the main idea?" Then answer the questions.

Tia is packing for her trip. She is leaving for New York in four hours. So far, Tia has packed her stuffed animals, her favorite books, and her new toys. Tia has also packed her rock collection and dolls. Her suitcase is almost full.

"All of your clothes are still on your bed," says Tia's mother. "There's no room in your suitcase for them."

"That's okay," says Tia. "I have the things I really need."

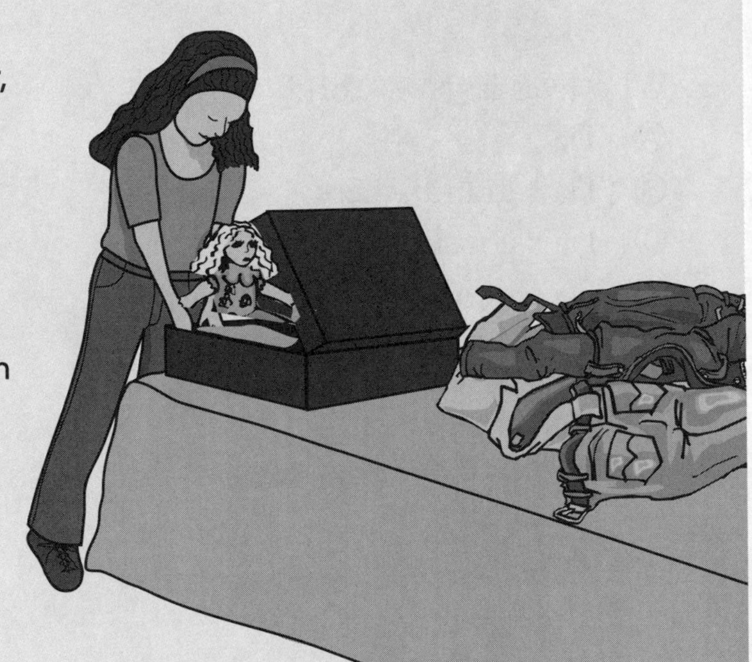

3. When is Tia leaving for New York?

Ⓐ in four days

Ⓑ in one week

Ⓒ in the morning

Ⓓ in four hours

4. Which detail tells about something Tia is packing for her trip?

Ⓐ Her suitcase is almost full.

Ⓑ Tia is packing for her trip.

Ⓒ Tia has also packed her rock collection and dolls.

Ⓓ "All of your clothes are still on your bed," says Tia's mother.

Look at the answer choices for each question. Read why each answer choice is correct or not correct.

3. When is Tia leaving for New York?

Ⓐ in four days

This answer is not correct because the second sentence tells you that Tia is leaving in four hours, not four days.

Ⓑ in one week

This answer is not correct because the second sentence tells you that Tia is leaving in four hours.

Ⓒ in the morning

This answer is not correct because there is nothing in this part of the story that tells about something happening in the morning.

● in four hours

This answer is correct because the second sentence is "She is leaving for New York in four hours."

4. Which detail tells about something Tia is packing for her trip?

Ⓐ Her suitcase is almost full.

This answer is not correct because it does not tell about something that Tia is packing in her suitcase.

Ⓑ Tia is packing for her trip.

This answer is not correct because it tells that Tia is packing, but it does not tell about what she is packing.

● Tia has also packed her rock collection and dolls.

This answer is correct because it tells about two things that Tia has packed in her suitcase for her trip.

Ⓓ "All of your clothes are still on your bed," says Tia's mother.

This answer is not correct because it tells about something that is not in Tia's suitcase.

PART FOUR: Learn More About Facts and Details

Facts and details help writers tell a story. Facts and details make a story more interesting. When you read, look for sentences that

★ describe a person, place, or thing.

★ tell the order in which things happen.

★ explain how to do something.

Read this article about metals. Then answer the questions.

Metals

There are many different kinds of metals. Most metals are bright and shiny. Iron is a metal used to make steel. Steel is important because it is needed to build cars, buildings, and bridges.

Gold and silver are also metals. They have been used to make jewelry and coins for thousands of years.

Most metals change when they are heated. When they are heated, they can be stretched or pressed. Wire is made by stretching and pulling metal. Aluminum foil is made by pressing metal into a thin sheet. Gold can also be made into a foil. But don't wrap your sandwich in it! Gold foil is expensive.

5. Steel is important because it is used to make

Ⓐ jewelry.
Ⓑ wire.
Ⓒ bridges.
Ⓓ gold foil.

6. Which detail tells more about the main idea of the last paragraph?

Ⓐ Gold and silver are also metals.
Ⓑ When they are heated, metals can be stretched or pressed.
Ⓒ Iron is used to make steel.
Ⓓ There are many different kinds of metals.

7. Most metals are

Ⓐ bright and shiny.
Ⓑ rough and dull.
Ⓒ long and thin.
Ⓓ hard and thick.

8. How is aluminum foil made?

Ⓐ by stretching metal
Ⓑ by pressing metal
Ⓒ by pulling metal
Ⓓ by tearing metal

Read this journal entry written by Mae. Then answer the questions.

Saturday, May 5

Today, Hal and I went to the school fair. There were lots of rides and games. There was also lots of food—hot dogs, popcorn, and fried dough. Hal and I had fun. He spent all of his money on food. I spent most of my money on games.

My favorite game was Dunk the Teacher. Ms. Ortiz, my favorite teacher, sat in a booth. Below her was a tank of water. I had three chances to hit a target. Any ball that hit the target would send Ms. Ortiz into the water. I couldn't help smiling as I threw each ball. Each one I threw hit the target! I hope Ms. Ortiz still likes me on Monday.

9. Which detail tells about Hal?

Ⓐ There were lots of rides and games.
Ⓑ I hope Ms. Ortiz still likes me on Monday.
Ⓒ I spent most of my money on games.
Ⓓ He spent all of his money on food.

10. What is a detail that tells about the main idea of the last paragraph?

Ⓐ Each one I threw hit the target!
Ⓑ There was also lots of food—hot dogs, popcorn, and fried dough.
Ⓒ I spent most of my money on games.
Ⓓ Today, Hal and I went to the school fair.

11. Ms. Ortiz is

Ⓐ Hal's teacher.
Ⓑ the school principal.
Ⓒ Mae's favorite teacher.
Ⓓ Mae's neighbor.

12. Which of these is a fact from the journal entry?

Ⓐ Mae spent most of her money on games.
Ⓑ Mae missed her target three times.
Ⓒ Hal is Mae's brother.
Ⓓ Hal's favorite game was Dunk the Teacher.

PART FIVE: Prepare for a Test

★ A test question about facts and details may ask you about something that happened in a reading passage.

★ A test question about facts and details may ask you about the *who, what, where, when,* and *why* of the main idea.

Read this story about Hector. Then answer questions about the story. Choose the best answer for Numbers 13 and 14.

"I'm going outside to play," Hector called to his father Saturday morning.

"Now?" asked Father. "Don't you want to wait?"

"Wait for what?" Hector asked as he ran out the door. Hector didn't hear his father laughing as the door slammed shut.

When Hector got outside, he looked around. First, he looked into the neighbor's yard to see if Alex was out. The yard was empty. Then he looked up the street to see if anyone was in the park. All he saw there was a bird pecking the ground for worms.

"What happened to everyone?" Hector wondered.

Finally, Hector looked at his watch. "I guess 7:30 is a little early to go out and play," he said to himself as he walked back to his house.

Recalling Facts and Details

13. Hector told his father that he was going

Ⓐ outside to play.
Ⓑ to the park.
Ⓒ to Alex's house.
Ⓓ back to bed.

Recalling Facts and Details

14. What did Hector see in the park?

Ⓐ a puppy
Ⓑ a friend
Ⓒ a bird
Ⓓ a nest

Read this article about the human body. Then answer questions about the article. Choose the best answer for Numbers 15 and 16.

A Different Kind of Machine

The human body is like a machine that never stops running. Every minute, your heart is beating. It pumps blood through your body with each beat. Your heart is always at work, even when you sleep.

Your brain is also always busy. It sends thousands of messages to other parts of your body. These messages travel at more than 100 miles an hour. These messages tell your ears about sounds. They also tell your eyes about pictures you see.

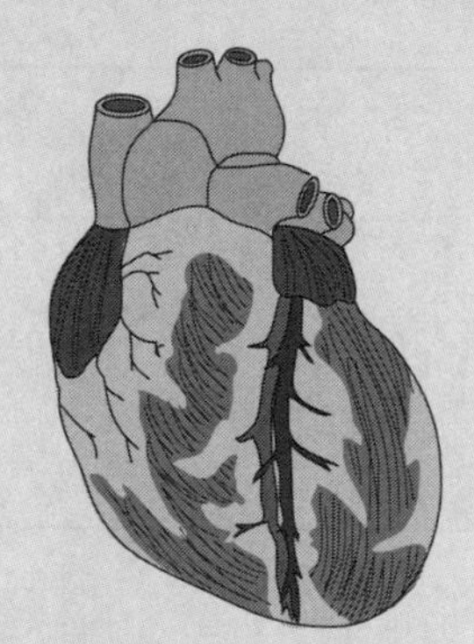

human heart

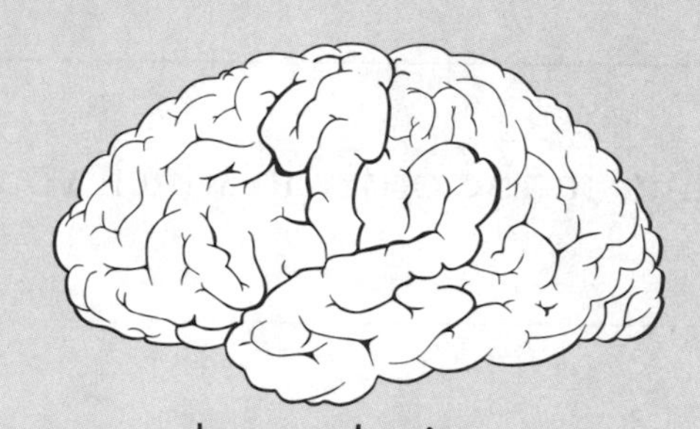

human brain

Recalling Facts and Details

15. Which detail tells more about the human heart?

Ⓐ Your brain is also always busy.

Ⓑ It pumps blood through your body with each beat.

Ⓒ These messages tell your ears about sounds.

Ⓓ The human body is like a machine that never stops running.

Recalling Facts and Details

16. Messages from your brain travel at

Ⓐ more than 1,000 miles an hour.

Ⓑ less than 10 miles an hour.

Ⓒ more than 100 miles an hour.

Ⓓ less than 1 mile an hour.

Strategy Three UNDERSTANDING SEQUENCE

PART ONE: Think About Sequence

WHAT IS SEQUENCE?

Many stories you read or movies you watch tell things in order. The stories have a beginning, a middle, and an ending. Sequence is the order in which things happen.

★ Write three things you do every day.

___

___

___

___

★ List these things in the order in which you usually do them.

___

___

___

___

You just wrote about sequence!

Tell your partner about one of your favorite stories. Take turns describing what happens in the story. Tell about the beginning, the middle, and the ending. Try to tell about each thing in only one sentence.

How Do You Find Sequence?

You can find the order in which things happen in a story by thinking about the beginning, the middle, and the ending. You can also look for words that tell about sequence. Some of these words are *first, next,* and *then*. Read the passage below.

> Yesterday, Marc had a fire drill at school. The bell rang and all of the students jumped out of their seats. Then their teacher told them to form a line. Next, they all walked outside.

Think about the order in which things happen in the story.

Let's find the sequence.

Look at the chart below.

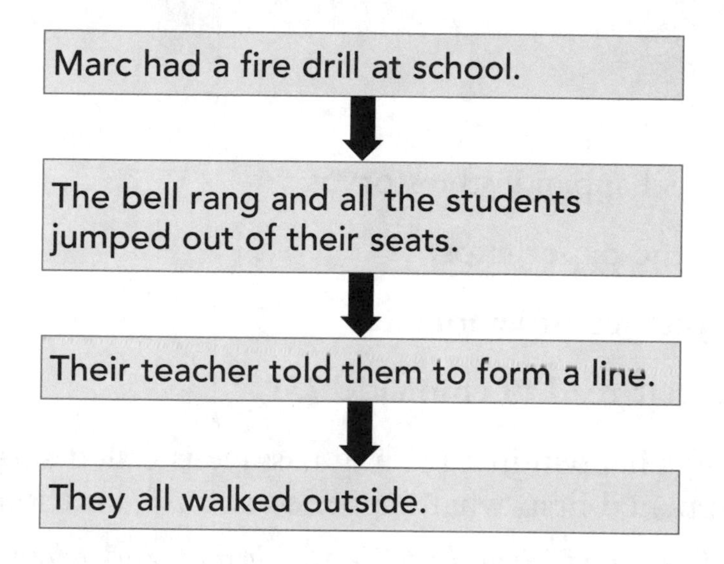

The chart tells the order in which things happen in the story.

> You just found sequence!

PART TWO: Learn About Sequence

Read the story about Aimee. As you read, think about the order in which things happen in the story.

Aimee's Big Idea

Aimee needed money to buy her father a birthday present. She had an idea. First, Aimee got out some paper cups. Next, she made a big pitcher of lemonade. Last, she made a sign that read "Lemonade 25¢."

The order in which things happen in the story is

First, Aimee got out some paper cups.

Next, she made a big pitcher of lemonade.

Last, she made a sign that read "Lemonade 25¢."

The order in which things happen in a reading passage is called **sequence**. Sequence tells what happened first, what happened second, and so on.

★ Clue words such as *first, next, then, last, finally, before,* and *after* often tell the order in which things happen.

★ Clues such as times of day, days of the week, months, and years tell when things happen.

★ Sometimes, there are no clue words. Thinking about the beginning, the middle, and the ending of a reading passage will help you understand the order in which things happen.

Read this article about how a snake sheds its skin. As you read, think about what a snake does first, second, and so on. Then answer the questions.

How a Snake Sheds Its Skin

As a snake grows, its skin becomes too tight. When this happens, the snake grows a new skin underneath the old one. When the new skin is ready, the snake sheds its old skin.

A snake follows several steps to shed its skin. First, the snake rubs against rough objects to rip its skin. Next, it crawls against the ground or through narrow places to strip off the skin. Finally, the outside layer of scaly skin comes off. This old skin looks like an empty snake!

1. What does a snake do first to shed its skin?

- Ⓐ It crawls against the ground.
- Ⓑ It rubs against rough objects.
- Ⓒ It goes off to a quiet place.
- Ⓓ It crawls through narrow places.

2. In the article, which clue word tells what the snake does last?

- Ⓐ first
- Ⓑ last
- Ⓒ finally
- Ⓓ next

Talk about your answers to questions 1 and 2. Tell why you chose the answers you did.

PART THREE: Check Your Understanding

Remember: Sequence tells the order in which things happen.

★ Look for clue words such as *first, next, then, last, finally, before,* and *after.* These clue words often tell the order in which things happen.

★ Look for clues that tell about times of day, days of the week, months, and years.

★ When there are no clue words, think about the beginning, the middle, and the ending of the reading passage. This will help you understand the order in which things happen.

Read this story about Kate and her brother. As you read, ask yourself, "What happened first? What happened next?" Then answer the questions.

Today is Saturday. Kate is baby-sitting for her little brother, Max. Max is two years old and very active. Kate has planned a busy day.

First, Kate is going to take Max to the library. Next, Kate will help him find books about dinosaurs. Max won't look at any books that don't have dinosaurs in them!

After they go to the library, Kate and Max will walk to the ice-cream store. Then they can eat their ice-cream cones and watch the ducks. Last, they will walk home. Kate and Max will cuddle up on the couch, and Kate will read to her little brother.

3. After they go to the library, Kate and Max will

Ⓐ go home.

Ⓑ read a book.

Ⓒ watch the ducks.

Ⓓ walk to the ice-cream store.

4. Which clue word tells what Kate and Max will do second?

Ⓐ first

Ⓑ next

Ⓒ after

Ⓓ last

Look at the answer choices for each question. Read why each answer choice is correct or not correct.

3. After they go to the library, Kate and Max will

Ⓐ go home.

This answer is not correct because this is what Kate and Max will do after they get their ice-cream cones and after they watch the ducks.

Ⓑ read a book.

This answer is not correct because this is what Kate and Max will do after they walk home.

Ⓒ watch the ducks.

This answer is not correct because paragraph 3 states that "After they go to the library, Kate and Max will walk to the ice-cream store. Then they can eat their ice-cream cones and watch the ducks."

● walk to the ice-cream store.

This answer is correct because paragraph 3 states that "After they go to the library, Kate and Max will walk to the ice-cream store."

4. Which clue word tells what Kate and Max will do second?

Ⓐ first

This answer is not correct because this clue word tells about what Kate and Max will do first.

● next

This answer is correct because this clue word tells about what Kate and Max will do second. Paragraph 2 states that "First, Kate is going to take Max to the library. Next, Kate will help him find books about dinosaurs."

Ⓒ after

This answer is not correct because this clue word tells about what Kate and Max will do third.

Ⓓ last

This answer is not correct because this clue word tells about the fifth thing that Kate and Max will do.

PART FOUR: Learn More About Sequence

Many reading passages tell details and events in the order in which they happened. Look for sequence in these kinds of reading passages:

★ stories, fables, and folktales
★ articles
★ directions
★ journal entries

Read this article about a steamboat. Then answer the questions.

The Steamboat *Virginia*

Long ago, steamboats traveled up and down the big rivers of America. One of the most beautiful steamboats was the *Virginia*. The *Virginia* traveled along the Ohio River.

The weather turned rainy on one trip down the river in 1909. It rained and rained and rained. The Ohio River soon began to flood. The fields on both sides of the river filled with water.

The rushing Ohio River carried the steamboat *Virginia* over its banks. The *Virginia* floated into a flooded cornfield. The bottom of the steamboat hit the ground. The steamboat was stuck!

Then the sun came out and the water soon went down. But the lovely *Virginia* was far from the river. The steamboat sat in the middle of the cornfield.

Finally, a crew of men dug the *Virginia* out of the cornfield. They dragged the steamboat to the river. The *Virginia* was now back in its true home—the Ohio River.

5. Which of these happened first?
- Ⓐ The steamboat was stuck.
- Ⓑ The weather turned rainy.
- Ⓒ The *Virginia* floated into a flooded cornfield.
- Ⓓ The *Virginia* was back in its true home.

6. After it began to rain,
- Ⓐ the river began to flood.
- Ⓑ the water went down.
- Ⓒ the sun came out.
- Ⓓ the steamboat went faster.

7. The clue word that tells you what happened last is
- Ⓐ *then.*
- Ⓑ *finally.*
- Ⓒ *after.*
- Ⓓ *next.*

8. What did the men do after they dug the steamboat out of the cornfield?
- Ⓐ They took a trip down the river.
- Ⓑ They waited for the rains to come.
- Ⓒ They left the steamboat in the field.
- Ⓓ They dragged the steamboat to the river.

Read this story about a family vacation. Then answer the questions.

The Chans went on a short vacation to the shore. They planned to go to the beach for swimming, boating, and fishing.

On Friday, they wanted to go boating, but it was too windy. On Saturday, they wanted to go fishing, but it was too rainy. On Sunday, they wanted to go swimming, but it was too cold. The Chans stayed indoors for three days. Before they go away again, they will be sure to find out about the weather!

9. In the story, clues that tell about the order of events are

Ⓐ days of the week.

Ⓑ times of day.

Ⓒ years.

Ⓓ months of the year.

10. What happened on Friday?

Ⓐ It was rainy.

Ⓑ It was windy.

Ⓒ It was cloudy.

Ⓓ It was cold.

11. What did the Chans want to do on Sunday?

Ⓐ stay indoors

Ⓑ go boating

Ⓒ go fishing

Ⓓ go swimming

12. Before the Chans go away again, they will

Ⓐ plan to stay away more than three days.

Ⓑ find a different place to go.

Ⓒ find out about the weather.

Ⓓ find a place where they can stay indoors.

PART FIVE: Prepare for a Test

★ A test question about sequence may ask you when certain things happened in a reading passage.

★ A test question about sequence may ask you to put events from a reading passage in order.

★ A test question about sequence may contain words such as *first, second, last, before,* or *after.*

Read this review of a new mystery book. Then answer questions about the book review. Choose the best answer for Numbers 13 and 14.

Night Sounds is Mary Reed's latest mystery book for young readers. The setting is an eerie mansion near the Maine shore. Gayle and Vic Brown are staying with their uncle, who lives in the mansion. The plot is about the strange sounds that the children begin to hear. They seem to be coming from inside the walls, and are heard only at night. The children tell Uncle Evan, but he doesn't seem to be worried.

Things soon begin to disappear, and the sounds get louder. When the children talk to Uncle Evan, he begins to act strange. The children decide to solve the mystery on their own. The things they discover will send chills up your spine!

If you like a good mystery story, read *Night Sounds*. But don't read it if you're alone in the house on a dark, stormy night!

Understanding Sequence

13. What happens first in *Night Sounds*?

Ⓐ The children begin to hear strange sounds.

Ⓑ Things begin to disappear.

Ⓒ The children decide to solve the mystery.

Ⓓ Uncle Evan doesn't seem to be worried.

Understanding Sequence

14. After things begin to disappear, the children

Ⓐ no longer hear the noises.

Ⓑ see their uncle acting strange.

Ⓒ solve the mystery.

Ⓓ run from the mansion.

Read this article about a well-known baseball player. Then answer questions about the article. Choose the best answer for Numbers 15 and 16.

Jackie Robinson was born in 1919. As a child, Jackie learned that not all people were treated the same. Because he was an African American, Jackie was not allowed to swim in public pools. He could sit only in certain places in movie theaters. Still, Jackie knew that he was as good as any other person.

Jackie joined the Brooklyn Dodgers in 1947. He became the first African American to play major-league baseball. Life was not easy for Jackie. Players on his own team called him names. Many times, he wanted to quit the team. But Jackie didn't quit. He stayed and helped his team win many games.

Jackie left baseball in 1957. He was entered into the Baseball Hall of Fame in 1962. He died in 1972. Jackie Robinson helped show that all people should be treated the same.

Understanding Sequence

15. Which of these happened first?

Ⓐ Jackie became the first African American to play major-league baseball.

Ⓑ Jackie was not allowed to swim in public pools.

Ⓒ Players on his own team called him names.

Ⓓ Jackie was entered into the Baseball Hall of Fame.

Understanding Sequence

16. The boxes show some things that happened in the article.

What belongs in the empty box?

Ⓐ Jackie learned that not all people were treated the same.

Ⓑ Jackie was born.

Ⓒ Jackie was entered into the Baseball Hall of Fame.

Ⓓ Jackie joined the Dodgers.

Strategies One–Three REVIEW

PART ONE: Read a Letter

Read this letter written by Gordon. Then answer questions about the letter. Choose the best answer for Numbers 1 through 6.

February 12, 2006

Dear Uncle Nate,

I wanted to thank you for coming to my school play, Life on the Farm. You may not know this, but this was the first time I've ever performed on stage. Boy, was I nervous. When the play started, I could feel my hands sweating and my heart racing.

I don't know if you noticed, but I forgot my lines several times. I don't think anyone heard my teacher whispering them to me across the stage. Did you like the way I tried to act natural when I tripped over the cows? I think everyone thought I was supposed to do that.

The best part was at the end of the play when we took a bow and everyone clapped.

Thank you again for coming to my play. I'll let you know when I'm in another one.

Your nephew,

Gordon

Finding Main Idea

1. The main idea of the first paragraph is found

Ⓐ in the first sentence.
Ⓑ in the last sentence.
Ⓒ in the middle of the paragraph.
Ⓓ by thinking about the most important idea in the paragraph.

Finding Main Idea

2. What is the letter mainly about?

Ⓐ a nervous nephew
Ⓑ a favorite uncle
Ⓒ a school play
Ⓓ a silly mistake

Recalling Facts and Details

3. Which detail tells that Gordon was nervous?

Ⓐ I could feel my hands sweating.
Ⓑ I tripped over the cows.
Ⓒ This was the first time I've ever performed in a play.
Ⓓ Thank you for coming to my play.

Recalling Facts and Details

4. Who helped Gordon when he forgot his lines?

Ⓐ his uncle
Ⓑ his teacher
Ⓒ his mother
Ⓓ his friend

Understanding Sequence

5. Which of these happened last?

Ⓐ The curtain rose.
Ⓑ Everyone clapped.
Ⓒ Gordon's heart raced.
Ⓓ Gordon tripped.

Understanding Sequence

6. You can tell the order of events described in the letter by

Ⓐ thinking about the beginning, the middle, and the ending.
Ⓑ looking for clue words.
Ⓒ thinking about the main idea.
Ⓓ finding the facts and details.

PART TWO: Read a Story

Read this story about a girl named Molly. Then answer questions about the story. Choose the best answer for Numbers 7 through 12.

Molly had always wanted a puppy. Stuffed dogs, pictures of dogs, and books about dogs filled her bedroom. But, she didn't have a dog of her own. Her mother said Molly would have to wait until she was eight years old.

Finally Molly's eighth birthday arrived. The next day, she and her mother went to an animal shelter to pick out a puppy. Choosing wasn't easy. The puppies were all so cute. Molly wanted to take them all home. After a long time, she chose a black and white puppy with blue eyes. She took him home and named him Zack. That night and every one that followed, Zack slept next to Molly when she went to bed.

Molly knew all about how to care for her new puppy. She'd been reading books for months. She knew that puppies need special food for their growing bodies and a fresh supply of water all the time. Molly also knew not to feed Zack the kinds of food people eat.

Zack was a Border collie. Border collies need lots of exercise. They are bred to herd sheep on farms. More than anything, Border collies like to run! Molly took Zack for lots of walks. Sometimes she got tired before Zack did.

Molly brushed Zack's coat every day. Zack loved having Molly run a brush through his thick fur. Molly also kept his coat clean. She used a special dog shampoo to give Zack a bath.

Molly's biggest job was to house-train Zack. Each morning she took him outside after he ate. She took him out again after school. She made sure that his last meal of the day was early in the evening. This gave Molly time to take Zack outside again before she went to bed.

As Zack grew bigger, Molly began to train him in other ways. When Zack did something he should not do, she would say in a firm voice, "No!" When he stopped doing what was wrong, she would pat him and say, "Good dog!"

Try as she may, Molly could hardly remember what life was like before Zack joined the family.

Finding Main Idea

7. The story is mostly about
   Ⓐ a puppy that finds a new home.
   Ⓑ a birthday present.
   Ⓒ a girl who cares for a new puppy.
   Ⓓ a puppy that needs to be walked a lot.

Recalling Facts and Details

10. What do Border collies like to do most?
    Ⓐ nap
    Ⓑ run
    Ⓒ eat
    Ⓓ play

Finding Main Idea

8. What is a good title for this story?
   Ⓐ "A New Member of the Family"
   Ⓑ "Zack's New Home"
   Ⓒ "How to Train a Puppy"
   Ⓓ "Molly Learns a Lesson"

Understanding Sequence

11. Which of these happened first?
    Ⓐ Molly went to an animal shelter.
    Ⓑ Molly wanted to take all the puppies home.
    Ⓒ Molly chose a puppy.
    Ⓓ Molly's eighth birthday arrived.

Recalling Facts and Details

9. One thing you should never give your puppy is
   Ⓐ lots of exercise.
   Ⓑ foods that people eat.
   Ⓒ fresh water all the time.
   Ⓓ a walk early in the evening.

Understanding Sequence

12. The boxes show some things that happened in the story.

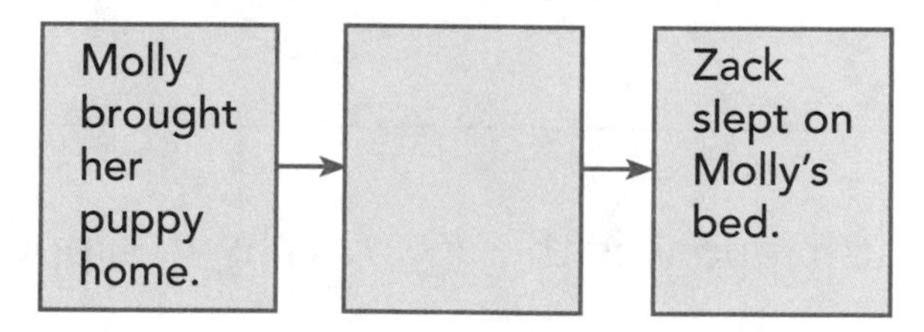

What belongs in the empty box?
    Ⓐ Molly read books about puppies.
    Ⓑ Molly gave Zack a bath.
    Ⓒ Molly patted Zack and said, "Good dog!"
    Ⓓ Molly named her puppy.

Strategy Four RECOGNIZING CAUSE AND EFFECT

PART ONE: Think About Cause and Effect

What Is Cause and Effect?

There is a reason for everything that happens. What happens is called the *effect*. Why it happens is called the *cause*.

★ Write what happens when students put too many books in their backpack.

___

___

___

___

★ Write why this happens.

___

___

___

___

What happens is the *effect*. Why it happens is the *cause*.

You just wrote about cause and effect!

Take turns giving each other examples of cause and effect. You might say, "I got wet in the rain because I forgot my umbrella." In each example, tell which part is the cause and which part is the effect.

How Do You Find Cause and Effect?

Not all reading passages tell about cause and effect. You can find examples of cause and effect by thinking about what happens in a passage and why it happens. Read the passage below.

> A great white shark was trapped in a small bay off Cape Cod. The shark was looking for food and got lost. Scientists helped the shark get back to the open ocean.

Think about the things that happened in the passage and why.

Let's find an example of cause and effect.

Look at the boxes below.

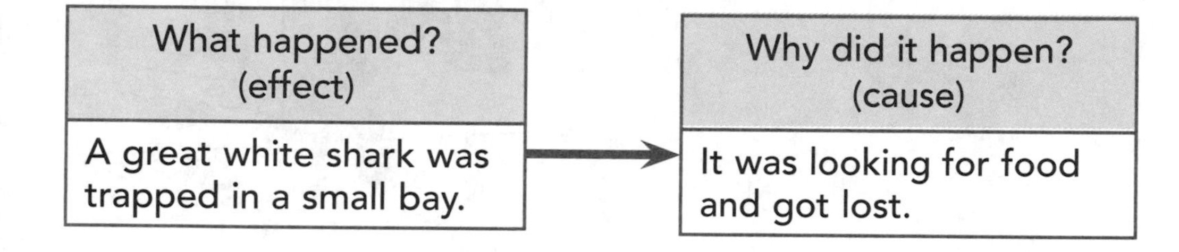

The first box tells what happened. This is the *effect*.

The second box tells why it happened. This is the *cause*.

Let's do another example.

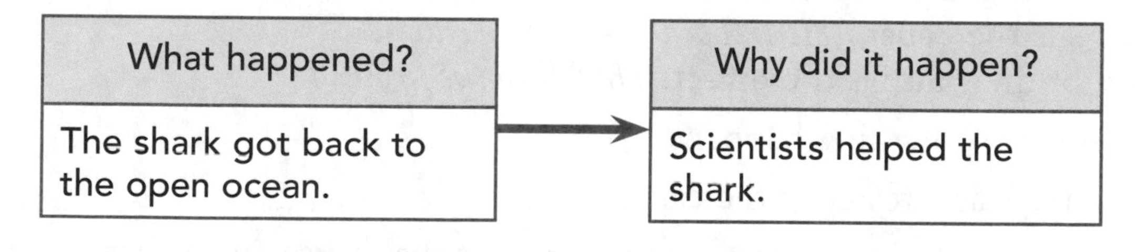

You just found cause and effect!

PART TWO: Learn About Cause and Effect

Read this story about Dan. As you read, think about one thing that happened to Dan and why.

Dan dressed quickly. He didn't want to miss the school bus. He grabbed his jacket, put on his shoes, and raced out the door. Oops! Dan forgot to tie his shoes! As a result, Dan tripped over his shoelaces and fell to the ground. Poor Dan! At least he didn't miss the bus!

One thing that happened to Dan and why is

What happened: **He fell to the ground.**
Why it happened: **He tripped over his shoelaces.**

What happens and why is called **cause and effect.**
Why something happens is the **cause**. *He tripped over his shoelaces.*
What happens because of the cause is the **effect**. *He fell to the ground.*

★ A cause is the reason that something happens.

★ An effect is what happens as a result of the cause.

★ Clue words such as *so, so that, since, because,* and *if* often signal cause and effect. Other clue words are *reason* and *as a result.*

Read this journal entry written by a boy who lives on a farm. As you read, look for clue words to help you understand what happens and why it happens. Then answer the questions.

January 28

I woke up this morning to two feet of snow. After breakfast, Father and I went out to feed the hungry animals. Since the snow was so deep, we had trouble getting to the barn. The animals must have been thirsty. Their drinking water froze into a solid block because it was so cold. We'll all be glad when spring comes!

1. The animals' drinking water froze because

Ⓐ it was so cold.

Ⓑ the snow was so deep.

Ⓒ the animals were thirsty.

Ⓓ the animals were hungry.

2. Which clue word or words signal the reason that the boy and his father had trouble getting to the barn?

Ⓐ because

Ⓑ as a result

Ⓒ so

Ⓓ since

Talk about your answers to questions 1 and 2. Tell why you chose the answers you did.

PART THREE: Check Your Understanding

Remember: What happens and why is called cause and effect.

★ To find a cause, look for a reason that something happened. Ask yourself, "*Why* did it happen?"

★ To find an effect, look for a result, or something that happened. Ask yourself, "*What* happened?"

★ Look for clue words that signal cause and effect, such as *so, so that, since, because, if, reason,* and *as a result.*

Read this article about the annual rings on trees. As you read, ask yourself, "*What* are some things that happen to trees? *Why* do these things happen?" Then answer the questions.

Annual Rings

Have you ever seen a tree that has been cut down? If you have, you probably saw the circles inside the trunk of the tree. These circles are called annual rings. You can tell how old a tree is by counting the rings.

Trees have rings because each year they grow a new layer of wood. This new layer grows beneath the bark. In a year with lots of rain and sunlight, the tree grows faster. The annual ring that year will be thick. If there is little rain or sunlight, the tree grows slower. The annual ring that year will be thin.

3. Why do trees have rings?

Ⓐ because they grow fast
Ⓑ because they are often cut down
Ⓒ because they get lots of rain and sunlight
Ⓓ because they grow a new layer of wood each year

4. If there is little rain or sunlight, a tree

Ⓐ grows faster.
Ⓑ grows slower.
Ⓒ has no annual ring.
Ⓓ grows a thick annual ring.

Look at the answer choices for each question. Read why each answer choice is correct or not correct.

3. Why do trees have rings?
   - Ⓐ because they grow fast
     This answer is not correct because trees grow fast when there is lots of rain and sunlight. This answer does not tell about the cause of the rings.
   - Ⓑ because they are often cut down
     This answer is not correct because this does not tell about the cause of the rings. Cutting down trees does not cause rings.
   - Ⓒ because they get lots of rain and sunlight
     This answer is not correct because trees have rings no matter how much rain and sunlight there is. The amount of rain and sun makes the rings either thick or thin, but does not cause the rings.
   - ● because they grow a new layer of wood each year
     This answer is correct because it tells the cause of the rings. The last paragraph states that "Trees have rings because each year they grow a new layer of wood." *The clue word* because *helps you recognize a cause and an effect.*

4. If there is little rain or sunlight, a tree
   - Ⓐ grows faster.
     This answer is not correct because a tree grows faster when there is lots of rain and sunlight.
   - ● grows slower.
     This answer is correct because the last two sentences explain that when there is little rain or sun, a tree grows slower.
   - Ⓒ has no annual ring.
     This answer is not correct because annual rings grow each year, no matter what the weather is. The ring may be thick or thin, but the tree will grow.
   - Ⓓ grows a thick annual ring.
     This answer is not correct because a tree grows a thick annual ring in a year with lots of rain and sunlight.

PART FOUR: Learn More About Cause and Effect

Sometimes, there are no clue words to show cause and effect in a reading passage. When there are no clue words, do the following:

★ To find an effect, think about *what* happened.
★ To find a cause, think about *how* or *why* it happened.
★ Think about what you already know about how one thing might cause another thing to happen.

Read this fable by Aesop. Then answer the questions.

The Boy Who Cried Wolf

There once was a boy who lived in a small village. Each day, he took his sheep to a high meadow to eat grass. One day, the boy was bored with his work. So, he decided to play a trick. "Wolf! Wolf!" he cried. "A wolf is here!"

The people in the village rushed to the meadow to save the boy and his sheep. They found the boy safe and laughing. "I was only kidding," the boy said. "There is no wolf here," he laughed.

"You are very naughty," the people said.

The next day, the boy played the same trick. And, once again, the people rushed to the meadow only to find the boy laughing.

A few days passed. The boy was in the meadow, when he saw a real wolf. "Wolf! Wolf!" he cried. "A wolf is getting the sheep."

The people in the village heard the boy's cries. This time, they did not rush to help him. They weren't going to be tricked again.

5. The boy took the sheep to the meadow so that they could
Ⓐ eat grass.
Ⓑ run in the meadow.
Ⓒ sleep in the grass.
Ⓓ play in the meadow.

6. Why did the boy cry "wolf" the first time?
Ⓐ He saw a wolf.
Ⓑ He was doing his job.
Ⓒ He needed help.
Ⓓ He was bored.

7. The people did not come the last time the boy cried "wolf" because they
Ⓐ were too busy working.
Ⓑ thought it was another trick.
Ⓒ did not hear the boy.
Ⓓ were afraid of the wolf.

8. Why did the people say that the boy was naughty?
Ⓐ They didn't like to laugh.
Ⓑ They didn't like funny jokes.
Ⓒ They didn't like his trick.
Ⓓ They didn't like the boy.

Read this article about two kinds of simple machines. Then answer the questions.

The Wheel and the Axle

Simple machines are useful because they help people do things that they could not do on their own. The wheel and the axle are two simple machines.

In a car, four wheels help move the car forward and backward. The steering wheel inside the car turns the two front wheels. When a driver turns the steering wheel to the right, the front wheels of the car turn to the right. When the driver turns the steering wheel to the left, the front wheels of the car turn to the left.

Many wheels, like the four wheels of a car, have a bar that is attached to the center of the wheel. This bar is called an axle. The axle causes the wheels to spin. Skateboards have axles. So do roller skates and bicycles. Look around you. Think about the simple machines that help you do things that you could not do on your own.

9. What causes the front wheels of a car to turn?

Ⓐ the engine
Ⓑ the steering wheel
Ⓒ the axle
Ⓓ a bar

10. Simple machines are useful because they

Ⓐ cause people to do things they would not usually do.
Ⓑ move the front wheels of a car.
Ⓒ help people do things they could not do on their own.
Ⓓ help wheels turn and spin.

11. What happens when a driver turns the steering wheel to the left?

Ⓐ The tires spin.
Ⓑ The front wheels turn to the right.
Ⓒ The car moves backward.
Ⓓ The front wheels turn to the left.

12. The part of a car that causes the wheels to spin is called the

Ⓐ axle.
Ⓑ front wheel.
Ⓒ steering wheel.
Ⓓ driver.

PART FIVE: Prepare for a Test

★ A test question about cause and effect may ask you *what* happened in a reading passage.

★ A test question about cause and effect may ask you *why* something happened.

★ A test question about cause and effect often contains words such as *because, why, reason,* or *what happened.*

Read this letter written by Juan. Then answer questions about the letter. Choose the best answer for Numbers 13 and 14.

September 29, 2005

Dear Ms. Frutt,

I have made an important decision. I have decided to quit third grade and return to your class.

It's not that I don't like third grade. The kids are friendly, and my new teacher, Mr. Lee, is nice. He lets us do experiments in class and tells funny jokes. He also lets us have a snake for a class pet.

My problem is that third grade is not as much fun as second grade. The work is harder, and we have homework every night. We have a math test every Friday, and we have to write a book report every other month. Besides, I miss my two best friends from last year. We were all together in your class. We are now in different classrooms. I miss second grade. So, I'll see you back in your classroom on Monday morning.

Your student from last year,
Juan

Recognizing Cause and Effect

13. One reason that Juan wants to quit third grade is that

Ⓐ he misses Ms. Frutt.
Ⓑ the work is harder.
Ⓒ the kids aren't friendly.
Ⓓ he doesn't like doing experiments.

Recognizing Cause and Effect

14. What happened to Juan's two best friends?

Ⓐ They each went to Mr. Lee's classroom.
Ⓑ They each went to a different school.
Ⓒ They each went to a different classroom.
Ⓓ They each moved to another city.

Read this article about travel in a land full of snow and ice. Then answer questions about the article. Choose the best answer for Numbers 15 and 16.

Winters are long in the Arctic. People who live there cannot grow crops on the frozen earth. They must find animals and fish to eat. Arctic hunters and fishers must travel across snow and ice.

Long ago, Arctic people learned how to build sleds. They built sleds with runners. Runners are blades on the bottom of a sled. The runners moved easily over the hard-packed snow. The runners were usually made out of wood. But few trees grow in the Arctic. Strips of animal bones and horns were added to make the wooden runners stronger. The Arctic people trained dogs to pull the sleds.

Today, people of the Arctic still hunt and fish. But snowmobiles have become more popular than sleds. Snowmobiles can go faster than sleds pulled by animals. And snowmobiles don't get tired or need to rest!

Recognizing Cause and Effect

15. Bones and horns were added to runners because they

- Ⓐ made it easier for dogs to pull the sleds.
- Ⓑ helped the runners move across the snow.
- Ⓒ caused the sled to go faster.
- Ⓓ made the runners stronger.

Recognizing Cause and Effect

16. Why are snowmobiles more popular than sleds?

- Ⓐ There are few trees to build sleds.
- Ⓑ Snowmobiles go faster than sleds.
- Ⓒ There are no animals to pull the sleds.
- Ⓓ Snowmobiles hold more people than sleds.

Strategy Five COMPARING AND CONTRASTING

PART ONE: Think About Comparing and Contrasting

WHAT IS COMPARING AND CONTRASTING?

Thinking about the ways two or more things are alike is called *comparing*. Thinking about the ways two or more things are different is called *contrasting*.

★ Write three things you and a friend or family member both like to do.

___

___

___

___

★ Write three things that you like to do, but your friend or family member does not.

___

___

___

___

You just wrote about comparing and contrasting!

Take turns telling each other something that is the same about both of you. Then tell something that is different about both of you. See how many likenesses and differences you can find.

How Do You Find Likenesses and Differences?

Not all reading passages compare and contrast two or more things. You can find examples of comparing and contrasting by thinking about the details you read. Read the passage below.

> Alma rides the bus to school each day. Hannah walks to school each day. Both girls are in the same class. They like to eat lunch together. Alma likes to play basketball at recess. Hannah likes to talk to her classmates.

Think about the details that tell about the likenesses between Alma and Hannah.

Now think about the details that tell about the differences between them.

Let's find the likenesses and differences.

Look at the boxes below.

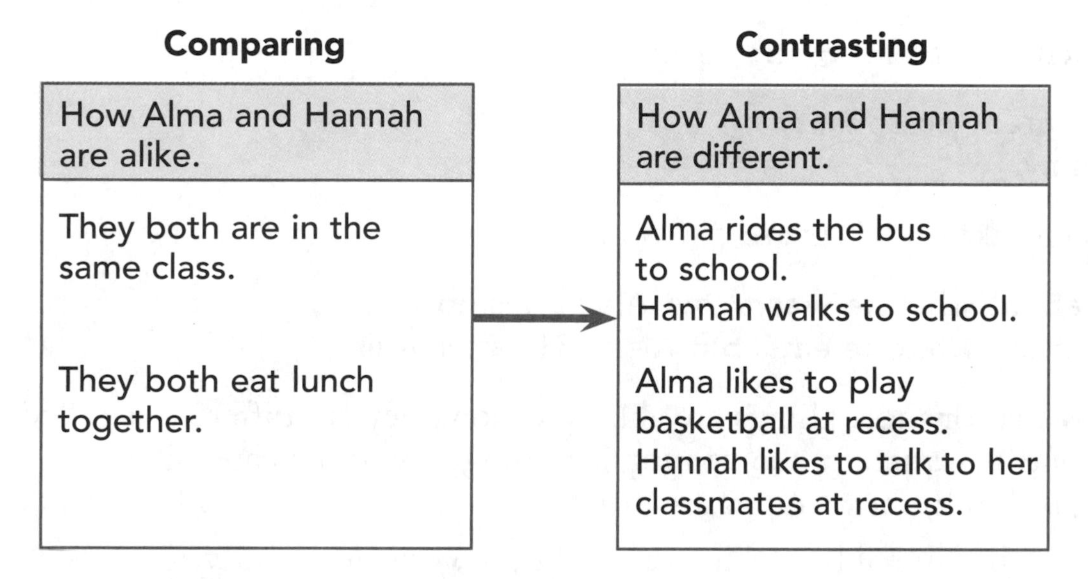

The first box tells about likenesses. This is *comparing.*

The second box tells about differences. This is *contrasting.*

> You just found likenesses and differences by comparing and contrasting!

PART TWO: Learn About Comparing and Contrasting

Read this journal entry written by Jake. As you read, think about the ways Jake and his friend Alex are alike and the ways they are different.

October 15

I sometimes wonder why Alex and I are friends. Alex has a great personality (like me!) and he's funny (like me!), but sometimes I don't understand him one bit.

Alex showed up at school today wearing the most horrible clothes. He doesn't care at all what he looks like. Me? I like to look good. Not Alex. He'll wear anything.

Then there are Alex's eating habits. He'll eat anything! Put it on a plate and put it in front of him, and Alex will eat it. Me? I care about what I eat. I try to eat healthful foods. I like broccoli pizza the best. But hold the milk. Better yet, give it to Alex. He'll love it!

Ways in which Jake and Alex are alike:

Both have a great personality.
Both are funny.

Ways in which Jake and Alex are different:

Jake cares about what he wears, but Alex does not.
Jake cares about what he eats, but Alex will eat anything.

Finding how two or more things are alike and how they are different is called **comparing and contrasting.** Comparing is finding how things are alike. Contrasting is finding how things are different.

★ Clue words that signal how things are alike are *same, like,* and *alike.*

★ Clue words that signal how things are different are *but, unlike, different,* and *however.*

★ People, places, objects, and events can all be compared and contrasted.

Read this passage about Russia. As you read, look for clue words that tell how Russia is like other countries and how it is different. Then answer the questions.

Both Russia and Canada are large countries, but Russia is the largest country in the world. Canada is the second largest country. Russia is almost twice as large as Canada.

Russia is unlike most other countries. It is one of the few countries that is on two continents. One part of Russia is in Europe. The other part is in Asia. When people at one end of Russia are waking up, people at the other end are going to bed.

Because it is so large, Russia has many different climates. In much of Russia, however, winter is the longest season. In the northern part of the country, cold weather can last for eight months. Winters there are dark and cold. There are many snowstorms. Sometimes people cannot leave their houses for days and days. Few people live in this part of Russia.

1. How are Russia and Canada alike?

- Ⓐ Both have a warm climate.
- Ⓑ Both are large countries.
- Ⓒ Both are in Asia.
- Ⓓ Both are on two continents.

2. Which clue word signals how Russia is different from other countries?

- Ⓐ but
- Ⓑ same
- Ⓒ unlike
- Ⓓ however

Talk about your answers to questions 1 and 2. Tell why you chose the answers you did.

PART THREE: Check Your Understanding

Remember: Comparing is finding ways that things are alike.
Contrasting is finding ways that things are different.

★ To compare, look for clue words that signal a likeness, such as *same, like,* and *alike.*

★ To contrast, look for clue words that signal a difference, such as *but, unlike, different,* and *however.*

★ Look for people, places, objects, and events that are being compared and contrasted.

Read this article that Todd wrote for a student newspaper. As you read, look for how things are alike and how they are different. Then answer the questions.

Skating in Hilltown

Most people were excited when the new indoor ice-skating rink opened last year. Before the rink was built, most people skated at the pond. But they could skate only in winter, when the water froze.

The people of Hilltown can now skate year-round. The Hilltown Rink is open from eight in the morning until eight at night. Most people say that they like skating at the new rink better than at the pond.

I guess I'm not like most people. I like skating at the pond. Sure, the ice is bumpy, unlike the smooth surface of the rink. And it does get pretty chilly. But I love the freedom of skating outside. On the pond, we can play hockey anytime. However, at the rink, only teams can play hockey.

The best part of the pond is the price. Skating at the pond is free. At the rink, skating costs five dollars!

3. In what way are the pond and the skating rink alike?

Ⓐ Both are bumpy.

Ⓑ Both are indoors.

Ⓒ Both are open until eight at night.

Ⓓ Both are used for skating.

4. Which clue word signals how playing hockey at the rink is different from playing hockey at the pond?

Ⓐ like

Ⓑ unlike

Ⓒ however

Ⓓ different

Look at the answer choices for each question. Read why each answer choice is correct or not correct.

3. In what way are the pond and the skating rink alike?

   Ⓐ Both are bumpy.

   This answer is not correct because paragraph 3 states that the ice at the pond is bumpy, not smooth like the surface of the rink.

   Ⓑ Both are indoors.

   This answer is not correct because a pond is found outdoors, not indoors.

   Ⓒ Both are open until eight at night.

   This answer is not correct because nothing in the article tells about the hours that the pond is open for skating.

   ● Both are used for skating.

   This answer is correct because people can skate at both places.

4. Which clue word signals how playing hockey at the rink is different from playing hockey at the pond?

   Ⓐ like

   This answer is not correct because the word like *signals that things are alike, not different.*

   Ⓑ unlike

   This answer is not correct because the word unlike *is used in paragraph 3 to tell how the surface of the pond is different from the surface of the rink:* "Sure, the ice is bumpy, unlike the smooth surface of the rink."

   ● however

   This answer is correct because paragraph 3 states that "On the pond, we can play hockey anytime. However, at the rink, only teams can play hockey."

   Ⓓ different

   This answer is not correct because this word is not used in the article.

PART FOUR: Learn More About Comparing and Contrasting

Sometimes, there are no clue words in a reading passage to signal how things are alike or how they are different. When there are no clue words, do the following:

★ Think about the people, places, objects, or events that you read about. Ask yourself, "How are they alike?"

★ Think about the people, places, objects, or events that you read about. Ask yourself, "How are they different?"

Read this article about two planets. Then answer the questions.

Jupiter and Earth

Nine planets travel around our Sun. Earth is one of these planets. Earth is the third closest planet to the Sun. Jupiter is the fifth closest planet to the Sun.

Jupiter is like a giant compared to Earth. Jupiter is the size of 1,000 Earths. Earth turns around once every 24 hours. Jupiter turns around in less than ten hours. It takes 12 years for Jupiter to go around the Sun one time. It takes Earth 365 days to go around the Sun one time.

Jupiter is covered by an ocean. Scientists believe the ocean may be 10,000 miles deep! But forget about swimming. You might get cold in your swimsuit. The temperature on Jupiter is much colder than that on Earth. On Jupiter, it is more than 250°F below freezing!

5. How is Jupiter different from Earth?
Ⓐ Jupiter is larger than Earth.
Ⓑ Jupiter is closer to the Sun than Earth.
Ⓒ Jupiter does not travel around the Sun.
Ⓓ Jupiter is warmer than Earth.

6. In what way are Jupiter and Earth alike?
Ⓐ Both are small.
Ⓑ Both turn around in ten hours.
Ⓒ Both travel around the Sun.
Ⓓ Both are the same size.

7. In the article, Jupiter is compared to
Ⓐ the Sun.
Ⓑ a star.
Ⓒ a planet.
Ⓓ a giant.

8. The temperature on Jupiter is
Ⓐ a little warmer than Earth's.
Ⓑ much colder than Earth's.
Ⓒ the same as Earth's.
Ⓓ much hotter than Earth's.

Read this story about two sisters. Then answer the questions.

"I'll never be as good a basketball player as you," Sam said. She slammed the basketball to the ground. "Never."

Jen, Sam's sister, picked up the ball. "That's not true. If you practice, you will get better. You already know how to dribble and how to pass and shoot. That's more than I knew at your age."

"Really?" Sam questioned. She wasn't convinced.

Jen nodded. "Yes, *really.* When I was eight years old, all I could do was shoot. And I couldn't even do that very well. I'm fourteen now. I've played six more years than you have. I've been on four different teams and practice three days a week. Once you join your team next week, you'll get better. It just happens." With that, Jen picked up the ball and tossed it to her sister.

Sam opened her arms to catch the ball. "I guess I better keep practicing," she said with a grin.

9. One way that Sam and Jen are alike is that they both

Ⓐ are going to join a basketball team next week.

Ⓑ like to play basketball.

Ⓒ have played basketball for six years.

Ⓓ want to be better basketball players.

10. One thing that Jen could do at age eight that Sam can also do is

Ⓐ practice.

Ⓑ dribble.

Ⓒ pass.

Ⓓ shoot.

11. Which of these tells one difference between Sam and Jen?

Ⓐ Sam does not play basketball as well as Jen.

Ⓑ Sam has been playing basketball longer than Jen has.

Ⓒ Sam likes basketball more than Jen does.

Ⓓ Sam practices more than Jen.

12. Which of these is true?

Ⓐ Jen plays many sports, and Sam does not.

Ⓑ Jen has played on fewer teams than Sam.

Ⓒ Jen is older than Sam.

Ⓓ Jen will always be a better player than Sam.

PART FIVE: Prepare for a Test

★ A test question about comparing, or likenesses, usually contains clue words such as *same, like,* or *alike.*

★ A test question about contrasting, or differences, usually contains clue words such as *different, unlike,* or *not like.*

Read this article about bears. Then answer questions about the article. Choose the best answer for Numbers 13 and 14.

There are about seven types of bears throughout the world. Only two types live in the wild forests of North America. These are the black bear and the brown bear.

Both of these large mammals live in forests. The black bear and the brown bear are also covered with fur and have big heads, short legs, and strong tails.

About 80,000 American black bears live in the northern forests of North America. They have black or dark-brown fur. Most American black bears grow to be five or six feet long and weigh up to 350 pounds. They are shy, and they usually hide from people.

There are a few thousand brown bears that live in the western forests of North America. Most brown bears have brown fur. Some have white fur mixed in with the brown fur. These bears are called "grizzly bears." Most brown bears grow to be about nine feet long and weigh up to 1,700 pounds. These bears are not shy. In fact, they can anger quickly and are known to chase people!

Comparing and Contrasting

13. How are black bears and brown bears alike?

- Ⓐ Both are shy.
- Ⓑ Both are short.
- Ⓒ Both live in forests.
- Ⓓ Both weigh about 350 pounds.

Comparing and Contrasting

14. One way that black bears are not like brown bears is that black bears

- Ⓐ are not found in North America but brown bears are.
- Ⓑ are dark brown and brown bears are white.
- Ⓒ grow to be longer than brown bears.
- Ⓓ hide from people and brown bears do not.

Read Eve's science report about two kinds of storms. Then answer questions about the report. Choose the best answer for Numbers 15 and 16.

Eve Thomas | Grade 3
Science | Mrs. Hale

Two Kinds of Storms

Tornadoes are storms that form over land. Most tornadoes happen in the middle of the United States. Tornado winds can blow up to 300 miles per hour. Tornadoes don't travel far, usually no more than 20 miles. In the United States, tornado season is from March until August.

Hurricanes are storms that form over the ocean. Most hurricanes happen in places along the coast. Hurricanes also have strong winds, but not as strong as a tornado's. These storms can travel for hundreds of miles. In the United States, hurricane season is from June to November.

Tornadoes usually last a matter of minutes. Hurricanes can last for days. However, hurricanes usually don't cause as much damage as tornadoes.

Comparing and Contrasting

15. The chart compares and contrasts tornadoes and hurricanes.

	Tornado	Hurricane
Alike	cause damage	cause damage
Different		

Which two things belong in the empty boxes?

Ⓐ strong winds/no wind

Ⓑ does not travel/travels hundreds of miles

Ⓒ lasts for minutes/lasts for days

Ⓓ form on land/form on land and at sea

Comparing and Contrasting

16. How are a tornado and a hurricane the same?

Ⓐ They both form over the ocean.

Ⓑ They both occur from March until April.

Ⓒ They both occur only in the middle of the United States.

Ⓓ They both are storms with strong winds.

MAKING PREDICTIONS

PART ONE: Think About Making Predictions

What Is a Prediction?

A prediction is a good guess about something that will happen at a later time. A prediction is often based on information you already know or have read about.

★ Write one thing you guessed would happen yesterday or the day before.

___

___

★ Write the clues that made you guess this would happen.

___

___

★ Was your guess correct?

___

★ Why do you think this was so?

___

___

You just wrote about prediction!

Tell each other something you thought would happen that actually did happen. You might tell about a surprise quiz you thought a teacher was going to give or news you thought you might hear. Take turns telling each other why you thought this would happen.

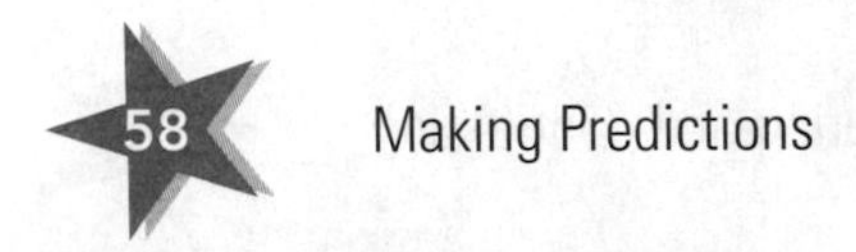

How Do You Make a Prediction?

You can make a prediction about a reading passage before you begin reading. Read the title of the passage below before you read the passage. The title gives you a clue about what you will be reading. Make one or two guesses about what you will find out as you read. Then read the passage.

> **The Birthday Puppy**
>
> Ty has always wanted a puppy. His mother told him that he had to wait until he was twelve years old. Then he could get a puppy of his own. Ty is eleven. His birthday is in two days.

Think about what the title tells you about the passage.

Let's make a prediction.

Look at the magnifying glass below. It shows the title of the passage.

Now look at the box. The box shows two good guesses about what the passage is about.

Think about the information in the passage. Choose the guess that is correct.

> You just made a prediction!

PART TWO: Learn About Making Predictions

Read the first part of this story about a girl named Jami. As you read, think about what might happen next in the story.

Jami jumped out of bed. She was so excited. Today was the Flag Day parade. Jami had never been in a parade before. But this year she was going to march with her third-grade class. As Jami got dressed, her little brother called to her. "Before you get dressed, you might want to look outside." Jami went to the window in her room.

Think about what you read and what you already know about parades. Make a good guess about what might happen next. Then continue reading to see how close your guess is to what actually happens.

"It's raining!" shouted Jami.

"That's not the worst part," said her brother. "It's supposed to rain for three days without stopping."

Jami knew there was no chance that the parade would still go on. Then she got the phone call from her teacher. The parade was cancelled.

What happened next in the story was **The parade was cancelled**.

When you think about what might happen next in a reading passage, you are **making a prediction**. Making a prediction is a way of using clues from a reading passage, as well as things you already know, to make a good guess about what might happen next.

★ Clues are often in the title of a reading passage. Read the title, and then make a prediction about what you will be reading.

★ Clues are often in the facts and details in a reading passage. Details about the things characters do and say often help you make a prediction about what they might do or say later in the story.

★ Clues are often in any pictures included with a story. Pictures often show something that is happening or will happen soon.

Read this story about story hour at a library. As you read, ask yourself, "What does the title tell me about what I will be reading? Which facts and details will help me predict what will happen next?" Then answer the questions.

Story Hour

Miss Dee is the storyteller at the library. Today, she is getting ready to read a new book. The children are seated on the floor around her storytelling chair.

"Does anyone here have a pet?" Miss Dee asked.

Billy raised his hand and told everyone about his cat, Snowball. Marta told a story about Rover, her dog. Liz talked about her goldfish, Bubbles.

Miss Dee asked the children if they knew anyone who had a pet dinosaur.

"No one could have a pet dinosaur!" Marta laughed.

"Well, let's see," said Miss Dee as she took a large picture book out of the bag next to her chair.

1. Which of these is most likely the name of the book that Miss Dee will read?

Ⓐ "Trains and Planes"

Ⓑ "Princess Polly Goes to Paris"

Ⓒ "Taking T. Rex for a Walk"

Ⓓ "Pioneer Family"

2. Where did you find clues to help you make your prediction?

Ⓐ in the title of the story

Ⓑ in the things Miss Dee said

Ⓒ in the details about the pets of other children

Ⓓ in the details about what Miss Dee took out of her bag

Talk about your answers to questions 1 and 2. Tell why you chose the answers you did.

PART THREE: Check Your Understanding

Remember: Making a prediction is a way of using clues from a reading passage, as well as things you already know, to make a good guess about what might happen next.

★ Look for clues in the details of a reading passage to help you make a good guess about what might happen next. Clues are often in the title, in the facts and details, and in any pictures.

★ Ask yourself, "What do I already know about the things I am reading about?"

Read this article about a popular author. As you read, think about the kind of books the author liked to write. Then answer the questions.

Have you ever met Brave Irene, Dr. DeSoto, or Sylvester the donkey? If you have, then you have probably read the books of William Steig.

William Steig began his career as a cartoonist. When Steig was 22, his father told him the family needed money. Steig thought drawing cartoons would be an easy way to earn some money. He was right. He soon sold a cartoon to the *New Yorker* magazine. Steig had a cartoon in the *New Yorker* almost every week for 60 years. That's close to 3,000 cartoons!

Steig wrote his first children's book in 1969. He has written many more books for children. The heroes of Steig's books are brave, clever, and full of hope. They are also very amusing. Ask your school librarian for books by William Steig. You'll be glad you did!

3. An author wants to write about the kind of heroes William Steig writes about. Her book will most likely include characters who are

Ⓐ silly and stupid.

Ⓑ tired and grumpy.

Ⓒ lazy and foolish.

Ⓓ smart and funny.

4. Which detail from the article helped you make your prediction?

Ⓐ The heroes of Steig's books are brave, clever, and full of hope.

Ⓑ Ask your school librarian for books by William Steig.

Ⓒ William Steig began his career as a cartoonist.

Ⓓ He has written many more books for children.

Look at the answer choices for each question. Read why each answer choice is correct or not correct.

3. An author wants to write about the kind of heroes William Steig writes about. Her book will most likely include characters who are

Ⓐ silly and stupid.

This answer is not correct because the last paragraph tells you that the heroes in Steig's book are brave, clever, and full of hope.

Ⓑ tired and grumpy.

This answer is not correct because the last paragraph tells about the kind of heroes in Steig's books. A hero probably would not be tired and grumpy.

Ⓒ lazy and foolish.

This answer is not correct because the last paragraph tells that the heroes in Steig's book are brave, clever, and full of hope. A hero would probably not be lazy and foolish.

● smart and funny.

This answer is correct because the last paragraph tells about the kind of heroes in Steig's books. Since some heroes are clever and amusing, a hero who was smart and funny probably would be included in the book of an author who wanted to write about the kind of heroes Steig wrote about.

4. Which detail from the article helped you make your prediction?

● The heroes of Steig's books are brave, clever, and full of hope.

This answer is correct because this detail helps you predict what kind of characters might be in future books.

Ⓑ Ask your school librarian for books by William Steig.

This answer is not correct because this detail does not give any clues about the kinds of characters Steig writes about.

Ⓒ William Steig began his career as a cartoonist.

This answer is not correct because this detail gives a clue only about one of Steig's other talents.

Ⓓ He has written many more books for children.

This answer is not correct because this detail gives a clue only about the number of books Steig has written.

PART FOUR: Learn More About Making Predictions

★ Think about what you already know about the things described in a reading passage. If you are reading about weather, think about what you already know about weather. If you are reading about a pet, think about what you already know about pets.

★ Link what you already know with the clues you find in the reading passage to make a good prediction.

Read this article about two brothers fishing on a lake. Then answer the questions.

"Look at the sky," Manny said as he cast his fishing line from the front seat of the canoe.

His brother, David, glanced upward. The bright sunlight of the morning sky was gone. In its place were dark clouds, moving swiftly across the blue sky. "Where did all of those clouds come from?"

Manny shrugged. "I don't know, but they sure moved in quickly." Manny looked over his shoulder. The clouds were turning darker. "It looks like the weather is going to change."

"I agree," David said. A strong, warm breeze blew across his face. He tightened the cap on his head. "I wonder how long we should stay out on the lake."

As David spoke, a flash of light lit up the sky. "I don't know about you," Manny replied, "but I think we should head home *now!*"

5. Predict what kind of weather will most likely occur next.

Ⓐ The sky will become sunny again.
Ⓑ Snow will fall on the lake.
Ⓒ Cold winds will blow across the lake and hail will start to fall.
Ⓓ Rain will fall from the dark clouds.

6. What will the boys most likely do next?

Ⓐ stay on the lake
Ⓑ paddle to shore
Ⓒ talk more about what to do
Ⓓ yell for help

7. Predict what would happen if the boys stayed on the lake.

Ⓐ They would catch many fish.
Ⓑ They would fall out of the canoe.
Ⓒ They would be in danger from the storm.
Ⓓ The weather would clear.

8. If the weather had not changed, the boys would probably have

Ⓐ gone swimming.
Ⓑ returned home.
Ⓒ continued fishing.
Ⓓ gotten into an argument.

Read this article about an unusual pet. Then answer the questions.

House Rabbits

A house rabbit is just that—a rabbit that lives in your house instead of outside or in a barn. You can even have an apartment rabbit. Rabbits are great pets because they like to be around people. They are very friendly and affectionate.

A rabbit that lives inside needs its own hutch. A hutch is a small rabbit house made of wire and wood.

Rabbits are very smart and very clean. Like a cat, a rabbit can learn to use a litter box. Put a litter box inside the rabbit's hutch. In just a few weeks, the rabbit will figure out how to use it.

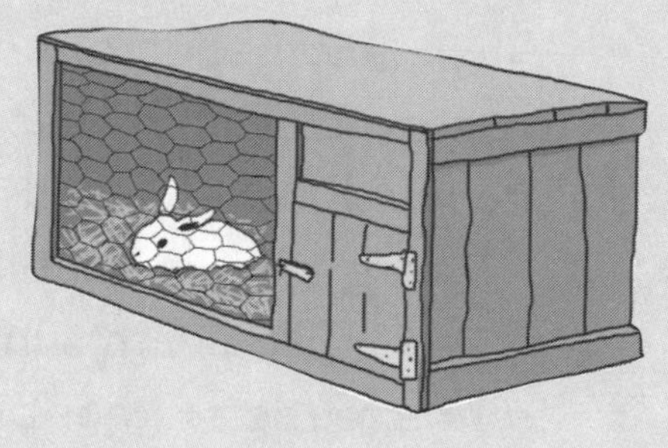

Rabbits are very curious, and they love to chew. They will chew anything! Before you let your rabbit loose in your house, give it a safe toy to chew.

9. Predict what would happen if you placed a toy rabbit outside the hutch near your pet rabbit.
   - Ⓐ The rabbit would ignore it.
   - Ⓑ The rabbit would sleep with it.
   - Ⓒ The rabbit would show interest in it.
   - Ⓓ The rabbit would be afraid of it.

10. If you were going to buy a pet rabbit, which book would probably be most useful?
    - Ⓐ "All About Wild Rabbits"
    - Ⓑ "Caring for Pet Rabbits"
    - Ⓒ "Floppy Bunny Goes to School"
    - Ⓓ "How to Train Your Pet"

11. Predict what would most likely happen if you did not provide safe toys for your pet rabbit to chew.
    - Ⓐ The rabbit would run away.
    - Ⓑ The rabbit would find something else to chew.
    - Ⓒ The rabbit would lose its teeth in time.
    - Ⓓ The rabbit would soon stop eating.

12. Who would most likely buy a pet rabbit?
    - Ⓐ Someone who doesn't like cats.
    - Ⓑ Someone who has a big yard.
    - Ⓒ Someone who lives in an apartment.
    - Ⓓ Someone who wants a loving pet.

PART FIVE: Prepare for a Test

★ A test question about making a prediction may ask you to make a good guess about what will happen next in a reading passage or what might happen in the future.

★ A test question about making a prediction usually contains the words *predict, probably,* or *most likely.*

Read this article about birds. Then answer questions about the article. Choose the best answer for Numbers 13 and 14.

Be Kind to Your Feathered Friends

Many birds in the wild depend on the kindness of people for their food. This is especially true in places where there are many homes and roads. When land is cleared to build new neighborhoods, many plants are destroyed. That makes it harder for birds to find food. If people don't provide food, the birds must find a new place to live.

There are several different ways to feed birds. One way is to put out a feeder filled with sunflower seeds or mixed seeds. Cardinals like to eat from a feeder. Other birds, like sparrows, prefer to eat seeds that have been scattered on the ground. In the winter months, birds need fat to help them survive the cold. To help them, take a large pine cone, spread it with peanut butter, and then roll the cone in mixed seeds. Add a string hanger, and place it on a tree branch. Try one of these ideas, or try them all. Don't be surprised if it takes a while for the birds to find the food. But once they do, they'll keep coming back for more.

Making Predictions

13. Predict what will probably happen the day after you hang a new bird feeder.

Ⓐ The seeds will sprout new plants.

Ⓑ Few, if any, birds will eat from it.

Ⓒ Sparrows will scatter the seeds to the ground.

Ⓓ Birds will enjoy the food within minutes of hanging the feeder.

Making Predictions

14. What would most likely happen if people stopped providing food for wild birds?

Ⓐ The birds would have to find different foods to eat.

Ⓑ The birds would die.

Ⓒ The birds would move to another area.

Ⓓ The birds would begin to eat other animals.

Read this story about two cousins in an unusual situation. Then answer questions about the story. Choose the best answer for Numbers 15 and 16.

Lin felt uneasy as she stood on the pitcher's mound. She could scarcely look at the batter, her cousin David. Though they had played baseball together many times at the park, Lin had never before pitched to David in a real game. At the park, David usually swung and missed whenever Lin pitched to him.

"Should I pitch easier to David than I have to the other players?" Lin wondered. "After all, he is my cousin. I would feel terrible if I struck him out, especially in front of all his friends."

Lin took a deep breath. Perhaps the idea of throwing easy pitches was not so good. "David and I have played baseball so often," Lin said to herself, "he'll know if I don't pitch my best. He would be upset if he thought I was taking it easy on him. Besides, he got two hits against the other pitcher. Maybe he can do the same against me." Lin knew what she had to do.

Making Predictions

15. Predict what Lin will do next.

Ⓐ She will throw the ball harder than she ever has.

Ⓑ She will ask her coach to get another pitcher.

Ⓒ She will pitch easily to her cousin.

Ⓓ She will pitch to her cousin as she would to any other batter.

Making Predictions

16. What will most likely happen if Lin pitches to David the way she usually does?

Ⓐ David will hit a home run.

Ⓑ David will strike out.

Ⓒ David will swing only at the slow pitches.

Ⓓ David will hit the ball farther than he ever has.

REVIEW

PART ONE: Read an Article

Read this article about a different kind of school. Then answer questions about the article. Choose the best answer for Numbers 1 through 6.

Long ago, there were few schools in the United States. Most children learned to read and write at home. As towns and villages got bigger, people began to build schoolhouses.

Many early schoolhouses had only one room. So, students of all ages were in the same class. Students who were six years old studied next to students who were twelve or thirteen years old.

A one-room schoolhouse had only one teacher. Most teachers were just a few years older than some of their students. The teacher sat at a high desk in the front of the class. This way, the teacher could see over the entire room.

A wood stove in the middle of the room provided heat. Students brought in wood from home. The walls of the classroom were black and sooty because of the smoke of the stove.

One hundred years ago, there were about 200,000 one-room schoolhouses in the United States. Today, there are only about 800. They are located in parts of the country where few people live. Alaska and parts of California are home to many of today's one-room schoolhouses.

Recognizing Cause and Effect

1. Teachers in a one-room schoolhouse sat at a high desk because

Ⓐ most of them were small children.
Ⓑ they wanted to be able to see the whole room.
Ⓒ they wanted to be treated like kings and queens.
Ⓓ they wanted students to be able to see them.

Recognizing Cause and Effect

2. Which clue word signals the reason that the walls of a one-room schoolhouse were black?

Ⓐ so
Ⓑ since
Ⓒ reason
Ⓓ because

Comparing and Contrasting

3. Teachers in one-room schoolhouses of the past were different from teachers today because they

Ⓐ sat at a desk.
Ⓑ taught students in heated rooms.
Ⓒ lived and worked at the school.
Ⓓ taught students of all ages in the same room.

Comparing and Contrasting

4. How are one-room schoolhouses like most large schools today?

Ⓐ Both are heated with wood stoves.
Ⓑ Both are places for learning.
Ⓒ Both have children of all ages in one class.
Ⓓ Both have only one room.

Making Predictions

5. Predict where you would most likely find a one-room schoolhouse today.

Ⓐ in the city
Ⓑ in a small town
Ⓒ near an amusement park
Ⓓ close to busy shopping areas

Making Predictions

6. An old one-room schoolhouse has been turned into a museum. Predict what you would most likely find in the museum.

Ⓐ a book about computers
Ⓑ a model of a spaceship
Ⓒ a classroom filled with children
Ⓓ a box filled with chopped wood

PART TWO: Read a Folktale

Read this folktale from China. Then answer questions about the folktale. Choose the best answer for Numbers 7 through 12.

The Painter and the Judge

Long ago, there was a judge who was very dishonest. He wouldn't even listen to what people had to say to the court unless they paid him a handsome sum. Even then, there was no guarantee that the judge would help. Sometimes he just took the money and did not give a fair hearing at court. Most people knew that the judge thought only of himself. He thought nothing of taking people's money.

A painter came to live in the same village as the judge. He had heard stories about how the judge cheated the townspeople. The judge had heard stories about the painter as well. He heard that the painter could paint pictures more beautiful than anyone had ever seen. The judge got a roll of white paper and went to look for the painter. He finally found him in the village square.

"You will paint me a beautiful picture," said the judge to the painter.

The painter did not want to do the work. He knew the judge would probably not pay him.

"I wish I had the time, sir," said the painter, "but I am very busy now. Perhaps another time."

But the judge would hear none of it. He begged the painter to paint a picture. Finally, he told the painter that he would hang the picture in the town square for all the important people to see. The painter decided that he would do the work after all.

A day later, the painter went to see the judge.

"I have finished your picture," he said, handing the judge the roll of paper.

The judge was overjoyed that the painter had done the work so quickly. He smiled with delight as he unrolled the paper, but his smile turned to a frown when he found no picture on the paper. All he saw were a few words that read, "Cows on Grass."

"Where is the grass?" asked the judge.

"The cows have eaten it," said the painter.

"Then where are the cows?" asked the judge.

"After they ate all the grass," said the painter, "there was nothing for them to do. So, they left."

Recognizing Cause and Effect

7. The painter did not want to paint a picture for the judge because
   - Ⓐ he didn't have any paint.
   - Ⓑ he couldn't think of anything to paint a picture of.
   - Ⓒ he thought the judge might not pay him.
   - Ⓓ he was too busy doing work for someone else.

Recognizing Cause and Effect

8. Why did the painter finally agree to paint the picture?
   - Ⓐ because the judge promised to hang the picture where important people would see it
   - Ⓑ because the judge paid the painter a handsome sum
   - Ⓒ because the painter feared the judge
   - Ⓓ because the painter decided he had the time after all

Comparing and Contrasting

9. How is the judge in the folktale different from most judges?
   - Ⓐ He listens to people.
   - Ⓑ He is rich.
   - Ⓒ He likes art.
   - Ⓓ He cheats people.

Comparing and Contrasting

10. How is the painting that the painter gave the judge different from most paintings?
    - Ⓐ It has no pictures on it.
    - Ⓑ It has real grass on it.
    - Ⓒ It shows cows eating grass.
    - Ⓓ It tells a story.

Making Predictions

11. What would someone most likely do if he wanted the judge to listen to him?
    - Ⓐ paint the judge a picture
    - Ⓑ offer the judge lots of money
    - Ⓒ write the judge a letter
    - Ⓓ cheat the judge out of money

Making Predictions

12. Predict what would probably happen the next time that the judge wants a picture.
    - Ⓐ He will try to paint the picture himself.
    - Ⓑ He will ask the same painter to do the work.
    - Ⓒ He will hire a different painter.
    - Ⓓ He will pay the painter a handsome sum.

Strategy Seven FINDING WORD MEANING IN CONTEXT

PART ONE: Think About Word Meaning in Context

What Is Word Meaning in Context?

Sometimes when you speak with someone, they use a word that you've never heard before. Many times you can figure out the meaning of the word by how the person uses it.

★ Write what you think the word *previous* means. It's okay if you don't know the real meaning. Just make a good guess.

___

___

★ Someone says to you: "<u>I like your new haircut better than your previous one.</u>" Write what you think the word *previous* means now.

___

___

★ Write the clues in the underlined sentence that helped you figure out what the word *previous* means.

___

___

You just wrote about word meaning in context!

Talk about some of the new words you have learned. Take turns using each new word in a sentence. Make sure your sentence gives a good hint to the meaning of the word. Have your partner guess what the new word means.

How Do You Find Word Meaning in Context?

You can find word meaning in context when you come to a new word in a reading passage. Look for clues to help you figure out what the word means. Clues might be in the sentence where the word is found. Clues may also be in the sentence just before or just after the one where the word is found. Read the passage below. See if you can figure out what the word *behave* means.

> Owls are best known for sleeping during the day and coming out at night to look for food. Raccoons also behave in this way. They sleep during the day and search for food at night. Can you think of any other animals that sleep during the day?

Think about what the word *behave* means.

Let's find the word meaning in context.

First, let's narrow down the clues.

The chart below shows three sentences: the one that comes before the word *behave*, the one that contains the word *behave*, and the one that comes after the word *behave*.

Look carefully at the sentences that come before and after the word *behave*.

Owls are best known for sleeping during the day and coming out at night to look for food.	Raccoons also behave in this way.	They sleep during the day and search for food at night.
Before		After

Now think about what the clues in the sentences tell you:

Raccoons behave like owls.
Owls sleep during the day and come out at night to look for food.
If raccoons behave like owls, they must sleep during the day and come out at night to look for food.

So, the word *behave* must mean ____.

> You just found word meaning in context!

PART TWO: Learn About Finding Word Meaning in Context

Read this story about Paul and his grandfather. As you read, think about the meaning of the word *launch* in the last sentence.

Paul and his grandfather build rockets together. Today they are going to try out the new rocket they made. Paul placed the rocket in the middle of the yard. Grandfather handed Paul the controls to the rocket.

"When you're ready to send the rocket into space, push the red button," said Grandfather. Paul smiled as he got ready to launch the rocket.

You can figure out the meaning of the word *launch* by looking at the words and phrases around it. The word *rocket* and the phrase *send into space* are clues to the meaning of the word *launch*.

The meaning of the word *launch* is "to send a rocket into space."

When you use clues in a reading passage to figure out the meaning of a new word, you are **finding word meaning in context**. The words and phrases around a new word often provide clues to the word's meaning. These clues are called **context clues**.

★ Context clues are often in the sentence where the new word appears. They can also be in the sentences before and after the word.

★ Clues about the meaning of a new word are often found by thinking about the way the word is used in the sentence.

★ Clues about the meaning of a new word can be found by thinking about the facts and details in the paragraph where the new word is found.

Read this poem about a butterfly. As you read, ask yourself, "What clues will I use to figure out the meaning of the word *hovering*?" Then answer the questions.

Butterfly Dance

Butterfly, butterfly,
hovering nearby.
Butterfly, butterfly,
floating in the sky.
Come rest on the flowers
that smell so sweet.
While you sip their nectar
and rest your feet.

1. The word *hovering* probably means
   - Ⓐ "smelling the flowers."
   - Ⓑ "soaring through the air."
   - Ⓒ "looking for flowers."
   - Ⓓ "moving but going nowhere."

2. Which phrase gives a clue to the meaning of the word *hovering*?
   - Ⓐ butterfly, butterfly
   - Ⓑ rest your feet
   - Ⓒ floating in the sky
   - Ⓓ come rest

Talk about your answers to questions 1 and 2.
Tell why you chose the answers you did.

PART THREE: Check Your Understanding

Remember: The words and phrases around a new word often give clues about the word's meaning.

★ Look for context clues in the sentence where the word appears. Look also in sentences before and after the new word.

★ Look for clues about the meaning of a new word by thinking about the way the word is used in the sentence.

★ Look for clues about the meaning of a new word by thinking about the facts and details in the paragraph where the new word is found.

Read this modern fairy tale. As you read, think about how you will figure out the meaning of any new words. Then answer the questions.

The New Princess

Once upon a time, there was a king and a queen. They were excited about the birth of their daughter. Fairies flew in from all directions to see the new princess.

The fairies looked at the sleeping baby. As they began to bestow beauty, charm, and grace upon her, they said, "Our gifts will help the princess become beautiful, charming, and graceful."

"Wait a minute!" announced the queen. "Of course, I want my daughter to be beautiful, charming, and graceful. But most of all, I want her to be herself. If she wants to be charming, let her practice her manners. If she wants to be smart, she can study. If she wants to be musical, let her take music lessons."

And so, with no help from the fairies, the princess grew into a lovely young lady.

3. In paragraph 2, the word *bestow* probably means

Ⓐ "look for."

Ⓑ "cover with."

Ⓒ "take away."

Ⓓ "give as a gift."

4. What is the best meaning of the word *charming* in the story?

Ⓐ "most beautiful of all"

Ⓑ "protected from harm"

Ⓒ "pleasing and polite to others"

Ⓓ "acting rudely"

Look at the answer choices for each question. Read why each answer choice is correct or not correct.

3. In paragraph 2, the word *bestow* probably means

Ⓐ "to look for."

This answer is not correct because the fairies did not come to the castle to look for something.

Ⓑ "to cover with."

This answer is not correct because the words and phrases around the word bestow *do not give any clues about the baby's being covered with anything.*

Ⓒ "to take away."

This answer is not correct because there are no clues that say that fairies took something from the baby.

● "to give as a gift."

This answer is correct because the words and phrases before and after the word bestow *tell about the fairies coming to the castle to bring gifts. You can figure out that the word* bestow *probably means, "to give as a gift."*

4. What is the best meaning of the word *charming* in the story?

Ⓐ "most beautiful of all"

This answer is not correct because the words and phrases around the word charming *tell that in order to be charming one would have to practice manners. Being the most beautiful of all has nothing to do with being charming.*

Ⓑ "protected from harm"

This answer is not correct because the words and phrases around the word charming *do not describe anything that would protect the baby from harm.*

● "pleasing and polite to others"

This answer is correct because the phrase "let her practice her manners" *is near the word* charming. *The phrase gives a clue about the word's meaning. You can figure out that someone who has good manners is probably pleasing and polite to others.*

Ⓓ "acting rudely"

This answer is not correct because the words and phrases around the word charming *do not describe ways of acting badly or rudely.*

PART FOUR: Learn More About Finding Word Meaning in Context

★ Look for a synonym, a word with a similar meaning, near a new word in a reading passage.

★ Look for an antonym, a word with an opposite meaning, near a new word in a reading passage.

★ Once you think you know the meaning of a new word, read the sentence where the word appears, using this new meaning. Does the sentence still make sense in the story? If so, you've probably figured out the meaning of the new word.

Read this article about swans. Then answer the questions.

Beautiful and *serene* are two words that come to mind when a peaceful pair of snow-white swans glide across a still pond.

"Absolutely wrong!" say some scientists. According to these experts, some swans are mean and nasty, especially mute swans. Mute swans are large birds. When they move into an area, they drive away smaller birds. They sometimes attack animals and people. Mute swans are also destructive. They cause damage to many kinds of plants. Mute swans eat four to eight pounds of plants a day. They even eat the roots. Many plants die and never grow back.

The number of mute swans in parts of the United States is exploding! In Massachusetts alone, there are twice as many mute swans now as there were ten years ago. This would be okay if the birds that looked so delightful weren't so unpleasant.

Officials in Rhode Island are desperate for help. Scientists there shake the nests of mute swans to keep the eggs from hatching. But they better watch out! Mute swans with eggs are even meaner!

5. In the first paragraph, which clue word is a synonym of *serene*?

Ⓐ beautiful
Ⓑ peaceful
Ⓒ pond
Ⓓ snow-white

6. The word *unpleasant* is in paragraph 3. Which clue word is an antonym of *unpleasant*?

Ⓐ exploding
Ⓑ desperate
Ⓒ mute
Ⓓ delightful

7. In paragraph 2, which word gives a clue to the meaning of *destructive*?

Ⓐ damage
Ⓑ people
Ⓒ plants
Ⓓ roots

8. The best meaning of *desperate* in the last paragraph is

Ⓐ "full of hope."
Ⓑ "in great need."
Ⓒ "dangerous or serious."
Ⓓ "willing to give up."

Read this story about two friends who find an unexpected surprise while walking. Then answer the questions.

A Cry in the Woods

Ada stopped along the side of the wooded path. "Did you hear that?" She asked her friend Hasan. "I think I heard something. I think it might be a voice."

Hasan strained his ears. A faint cry of "help" seemed to echo in the woods. "I hear it too!" he exclaimed.

"Follow me," Ada said as she burst down the path. "There's a clearing up ahead. We'll be able to see what's going on from there." Hasan hurried to stay close behind.

Together, the two friends followed the sound. When they arrived at the field, their eyes grew large and their tired legs came to a sudden stop.

There, in the clearing, were three small children, whimpering. They seemed tired and afraid. "We better help them," Ada said as she marched across the clearing. "They look as if they have been lost for hours."

9. In paragraph 2, you can tell that *faint* means

Ⓐ "fearful."
Ⓑ "loud."
Ⓒ "easy to find."
Ⓓ "hard to hear."

10. In paragraph 3, which word gives a clue to the meaning of *burst*?

Ⓐ path
Ⓑ clearing
Ⓒ hurried
Ⓓ behind

11. Which clue word is a synonym of *clearing*?

Ⓐ path
Ⓑ field
Ⓒ sound
Ⓓ cry

12. In the last paragraph, the best meaning of the word *whimpering* is

Ⓐ "yelling loudly."
Ⓑ "shaking with fear."
Ⓒ "crying softly."
Ⓓ "jumping happily."

PART FIVE: Prepare for a Test

★ A test question about finding meaning in context asks you about the meaning of a word as it is used in a reading passage. Some words have more than one meaning. Be sure you choose the correct meaning for the way the word is used in the passage.

★ A test question about finding meaning in context usually has several answer choices. Try each answer choice in the sentence in which the word appears. Decide which answer choice makes the most sense in the reading passage.

Read this song written by a cowboy. Then answer questions about the song. Choose the best answer for Numbers 13 and 14.

Red River Valley

From this valley they say you are going;
We will miss your bright eyes and sweet smile,
For they say you are taking the sunshine
That has brightened our pathway awhile.

Come and sit by my side if you love me.
Do not hasten to bid me **adieu**,
But remember the Red River Valley
And the cowboy that loves you so true.

Won't you think of this valley you're leaving?
Oh, how lonely, how sad it will be.
Oh, think of the fond heart you're breaking
And the grief you are causing me.

adieu: a French word meaning "good-bye"

Finding Word Meaning in Context

13. In the song, the word *hasten* means

Ⓐ "come back again."
Ⓑ "stop suddenly."
Ⓒ "act quickly."
Ⓓ "whisper."

Finding Word Meaning in Context

14. In the last line, what is the best meaning of *grief*?

Ⓐ "love"
Ⓑ "sadness"
Ⓒ "peace"
Ⓓ "happiness"

Read this article written by a student for a school newspaper. Then answer questions about the article. Choose the best answer for Numbers 15 and 16.

Students Need More Recess

by Carla Gonzalez

How many of you noticed that recess was cut by ten minutes this year? Last year, recess lasted twenty minutes. But this year, recess is only half that time.

Why the change? Well, I posed the question to our principal, Ms. Bates, last week.

"A new law was passed over the summer," explained Ms. Bates. "The law states that students need to spend more time learning in the classroom. As a result, the amount of time for daily recess had to be decreased."

So what can students do about this? Talk to your parents. Explain to them how important it is for us to have a longer recess. Students need to talk, run, and have fun. Recess helps us stay fit. Recess also helps us pay better attention during class. Ask them to help schools solve the time problem. Maybe then, we can get the twenty minutes of recess we need!

Finding Word Meaning in Context

15. In paragraph 2, *posed* means

Ⓐ "requested."
Ⓑ "modeled."
Ⓒ "presented."
Ⓓ "answered."

Finding Word Meaning in Context

16. The best meaning of the word *decreased* is

Ⓐ "made less or smaller."
Ⓑ "done away with."
Ⓒ "changed again."
Ⓓ "found inside."

Strategy Eight DRAWING CONCLUSIONS AND MAKING INFERENCES

PART ONE: Think About Drawing Conclusions and Making Inferences

WHAT ARE CONCLUSIONS AND INFERENCES?

There are many times each day when you figure out something on your own without being told what is happening. If you see someone crying, you know that the person is sad. If you hear someone laughing, you know that the person just heard something funny.

★ Write what you think would happen if you walked home in the rain without a raincoat or an umbrella.

____

____

____

____

★ Write why you think this would happen.

____

____

____

____

You just wrote about drawing conclusions and making inferences!

Take turns asking each other "What might happen?" questions. Ask questions such as, "What might happen if a funnel cloud formed in the sky?" or "What might happen if you found a dinosaur fossil in your backyard?" Let your imagination go!

How Do You Draw Conclusions and Make Inferences?

There are many times when you read that you draw conclusions or make inferences. Sometimes the author does not give you all the details. You need to figure something out by yourself. An author might write about a sunset. The author does not need to tell you what time of day it is. You can figure this out on your own. Read the passage below. See what you can figure out on your own.

> Mrs. McGuffin's dog barks every night, all night long. The dog is very large and very loud. Mrs. McGuffin's neighbors cannot sleep.

Think about what the author tells you.

Let's draw a conclusion.

First, let's narrow down the clues.

The passage tells you three things.

These three things are listed in the first box below.

Now think about the information the author does not tell you.

What information can you figure out on your own?

What does the passage tell you?	What information does the author leave out?	What information can you figure out on your own?
Mrs. McGuffin's dog barks every night. The dog is very large and very loud. Mrs. McGuffin's neighbors cannot sleep.	The author does not tell why Mrs. McGuffin's neighbors cannot sleep.	Mrs. McGuffin's neighbors cannot sleep because ________________ ________________ ________________.

You just worked with drawing conclusions and making inferences!

PART TWO: Learn About Drawing Conclusions and Making Inferences

Read this story about a girl named Ana. As you read, try to figure out why the crowd is cheering at the end of the story.

Today was the day of the big gymnastics meet. It was Ana's turn on the balance beam. For months, Ana had been practicing her routine. But practice was one thing. There were hundreds of people here at the meet! Ana spotted her family sitting in the stands. They gave her an encouraging wave.

Ana got on the balance beam. Everything was going so well—her split, her forward roll, and her cartwheel. Now for the back flip! Ana could hear the crowd cheer. The hours of practice had been worth it.

This story does not tell you why the crowd was cheering. It does, however, give you details that help you figure out why this happened.

Everything was going so well.
The hours of practice had been worth it.

These details help you figure out that Ana's back flip was successful. Her routine started well. When she was done, she felt that the practice had been worth it. You probably know from your own experiences that by practicing something, you learn to do it better. You probably also know that people cheer when something good happens.

Information is not always clearly stated in a reading passage. You must figure out some information on your own. Whenever you figure out something that is not told in a reading passage, you are **drawing a conclusion** or **making an inference**.

★ Pay attention to the details in a reading passage. You can use these details to figure out information that is not clearly stated.

★ Use the details from the reading passage and what you know from your own life to draw a conclusion or to make an inference.

Read this sign about a town event. As you read, look for details that help you figure out some of things people can do at the event. Then answer the questions.

Farmer's Market

Every Saturday
on the Town Common
8:00 A.M. to 3:00 P.M.

Shop for fresh fruits and vegetables
at over 25 booths from local farms.
Swap recipes at the Cook's Table.
Buy fresh breads, cakes, and cookies.
Bring the family!

Farmers will show children how to plant and care for a garden.
Children will learn about the parts of plants they can eat.
Have children bring a small container and soil.
Children will be given vegetable seeds.

1. From the sign, you can tell that
- Ⓐ children are not welcome.
- Ⓑ children can plant seeds.
- Ⓒ all plants are used for food.
- Ⓓ all farmers are selling bread.

2. Which detail from the sign helps you answer question 1?
- Ⓐ Swap recipes at the Cook's Table.
- Ⓑ Bring the family!
- Ⓒ Children will learn about the parts of plants they can eat.
- Ⓓ Have children bring a small container and soil.

Talk about your answers to questions 1 and 2.
Tell why you chose the answers you did.

PART THREE: Check Your Understanding

Remember: Drawing a conclusion or making an inference is a way of figuring out information that is not stated in a reading passage.

★ Think about the details that are stated in a reading passage. Use these details to help you figure out information that is not explained.

★ Use the details from the reading passage and what you know from your own life to draw a conclusion or to make an inference.

Read this fable about a crow. As you read, ask yourself, "What information can I figure out on my own?" Then answer the questions.

There once was a crow that thought he was treated very unfairly. Every day, he watched while the farmer threw out food for the doves to eat. The crow, on the other hand, had to scratch and search for every bite of food. "This isn't fair," thought the crow. He decided to do something about it.

The crow covered himself with white powder. Then he quietly entered the dovecote. The doves thought the crow was one of them. They greeted him and shared their food with him. "This is the life!" thought the crow. Everything went smoothly until one day when the crow spoke, and let out a very crowlike, "Caw! Caw! Caw!" The doves realized at once that this new bird was a crow and not a dove. They chased him out of the dovecote.

The crow tried to return to live with the other crows. But the crows did not recognize the white bird. They wanted nothing to do with him.

3. The crow covered himself with white powder so that he

Ⓐ could trick the farmer.

Ⓑ would look like a dove.

Ⓒ would be liked by other crows.

Ⓓ could steal food from other birds.

4. You can figure out that

Ⓐ crows look very much like doves, except for their color.

Ⓑ doves and crows make the same sounds.

Ⓒ doves do not like to share their food.

Ⓓ crows never have enough food to eat.

Look at the answer choices for each question. Read why each answer choice is correct or not correct.

3. The crow covered himself with white powder so that he

Ⓐ could trick the farmer.

This answer is not correct because the details in the fable show that the crow was trying to trick the other doves, not the farmer.

● would look like a dove.

This answer is correct because after the crow covered himself with white powder, he went to the dovecote. You can figure out from this detail that the crow must have thought that covering himself with white powder would make him look like a dove.

Ⓒ would be liked by other crows.

This answer is not correct because there are no details that tell about the crow not being liked by other crows. At the end of the fable, the crows want nothing to do with him only because they don't recognize him.

Ⓓ could steal food from other birds.

This answer is not correct because there are no details that tell that the crow wanted to steal in order to get the food he needed.

4. You can figure out that

● crows look very much like doves, except for their color.

This answer is correct because after the crow covered himself with white powder, the doves thought that he was a dove. You can figure out that crows and doves must look very much alike, except for their color.

Ⓑ doves and crows make the same sounds.

This answer is not correct because the details in the fable tell you that once the crow spoke and made a crowlike sound, the doves knew he wasn't one of them. You can figure out from this detail that doves and crows do not make the same sounds.

Ⓒ doves do not like to share their food.

This answer is not correct because the details explain that doves do share their food, but only with other doves.

Ⓓ crows never have enough food to eat.

This answer is not correct because the details tell about only one crow who is upset that the farmer never puts out food for him.

PART FOUR: Learn More About Drawing Conclusions and Making Inferences

★ Look for details in a reading passage that tell about the way a person or character looks, acts, thinks, feels, and speaks. Think about how people with similar qualities act.

★ Think about where something happens or when it happens in a reading passage. If something happens near the Statue of Liberty, you can figure out that the setting is New York. If something happens as the sun is rising, you can figure out that it is morning.

Read this article about a girl who visits her family in India. Then answer the questions.

Shalini was born in India. She grew up in America with her mother and father. Her family moved to New York when her father got a new job. They left India for their new home in America when Shalini was four years old.

Most of Shalini's family still lives in India. She has not seen her grandparents, aunts, uncles, or cousins for a long time. Shalini just returned from a visit to India. She met her cousin Yatish for the first time.

"Yatish and his family are Hindu, like me," says Shalini. "They do not eat most meat or any fish. They do eat chicken, eggs, and cheese."

Shalini will return to India next summer. She will stay with her grandparents and spend eight weeks with them. "I can't wait," says Shalini. "I love living in America, but India is also my home."

5. You can tell from the article that Yatish

Ⓐ does not care about what he eats.

Ⓑ eats only certain foods.

Ⓒ eats whatever foods he wants.

Ⓓ does not enjoy eating pizza.

6. A good meal to serve Yatish would be

Ⓐ hamburgers and fries.

Ⓑ spaghetti and meatballs.

Ⓒ steak and mashed potatoes.

Ⓓ chicken and rice.

7. From the article, you can tell that Shalini

Ⓐ was born in America.

Ⓑ lives with her cousin.

Ⓒ lives in India.

Ⓓ will return to India.

8. There is enough information in the article to show that

Ⓐ chicken is not eaten by people who are Hindu.

Ⓑ there is no meat available in India.

Ⓒ Yatish had never met Shalini.

Ⓓ Shalini likes to eat lots of fish.

Read this article about the country of Japan. Then answer the questions.

Japan is an island country in Asia. Japan is made up of four large islands and over 3,000 smaller ones. The main islands are Hokkaido, Honshu, Shikoku, and Kyushu.

Japan is a small country with a large population. Mountains cover much of Japan. This land cannot be developed for homes. It is also not good for farming. Most people live close together in cities near the ocean. This makes some areas of Japan very crowded.

Japan has many interesting and unique features. Mount Fuji is the highest point in Japan. It is a volcano that has not erupted in 250 years. The Kanto Plain is the largest area of flat land in Japan. This plain is home to Japan's capital city, Tokyo.

The first people settled in Japan more than 8,000 years ago. Over time, they came to call their country Nippon. This name means "Land of the Rising Sun." Nippon is the name that is still used in Japan today.

9. From the article, you can tell that Japan has
- Ⓐ few cities.
- Ⓑ few farms.
- Ⓒ few people.
- Ⓓ few islands.

10. Details in the article suggest that Japan is
- Ⓐ larger than the United States.
- Ⓑ made up of many plains.
- Ⓒ surrounded by water.
- Ⓓ home to the largest plain in the world.

11. What can you conclude about Mt. Fuji from the article?
- Ⓐ It is located in Tokyo.
- Ⓑ It is an active volcano.
- Ⓒ It is the highest mountain in the world.
- Ⓓ It is not an active volcano.

12. Which of these would you probably <u>not</u> find in Japan?
- Ⓐ large numbers of people
- Ⓑ tall office buildings
- Ⓒ large areas of flat land
- Ⓓ busy ocean cities

★ A test question about drawing conclusions or making inferences asks you to figure out something that is not stated in a reading passage.

★ A test question about drawing conclusions or making inferences often contains the words *you can tell*, *determine*, or *conclude*.

Read this story about an unusual event. Then answer questions about the story. Choose the best answer for Numbers 13 and 14.

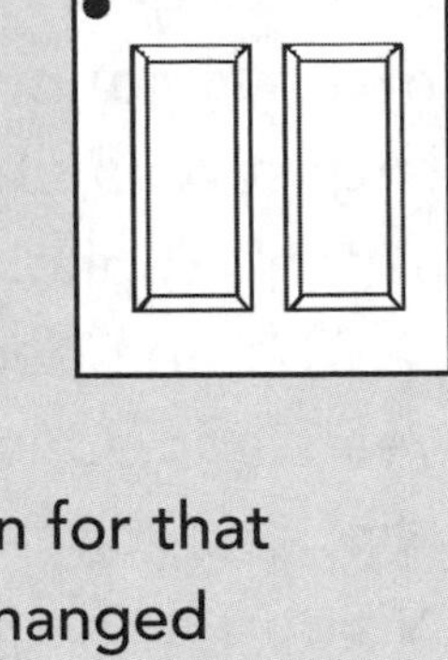

"I'd be careful if I were you," a soft voice called as Sara prepared to open the closet door.

Sara turned around, but no one else was in the room. There was only a tall grandfather clock, a few pieces of furniture, and a large window that filled the room with a hint of moonlight. "Who said that?" Sara asked, confused.

"I did," said the clock.

Sara's eyes widened. She approached the clock and said, "You? *You* spoke to me?"

"I think I must tell you about the door you almost opened. See that sign on the door that says OPEN CAREFULLY? There is a reason for that sign. That door is no ordinary door. If you open it, your life will be changed forever. So, remember—open it *carefully*."

"Thanks for the warning," Sara said as she placed her hand on the doorknob. She paused for a moment and then removed her hand. After a few minutes, she reached for the doorknob again. Slowly, Sara opened the door. Almost immediately, a brilliant light poured into the room. Within seconds, Sara arrived in a strange and magical world.

Drawing Conclusions and Making Inferences

13. You can tell that the story takes place

Ⓐ long ago.
Ⓑ at night.
Ⓒ in a castle.
Ⓓ at dawn.

Drawing Conclusions and Making Inferences

14. You can figure out that Sara

Ⓐ was afraid of the talking clock.
Ⓑ wished she had not opened the door.
Ⓒ almost changed her mind about opening the door.
Ⓓ did not see the sign on the door.

Read this folktale from Africa. Then answer questions about the folktale. Choose the best answer for Numbers 15 and 16.

Some time ago, a baby snake set out to play. As he slithered away, his mother spoke this rhyme: "Watch out young son, for things with claws, for things with a beak, for things with strong jaws."

"Claws, beak, jaws. Claws, beak, jaws," Snake Baby repeated.

At the same time, a baby frog set out to play. As he hopped away, his mother spoke this rhyme: "Watch out for the hiss, watch out for the coil, watch out for the squeeze, they will cause turmoil."

"Hiss, coil, squeeze. Hiss, coil, squeeze," Frog Baby repeated.

Snake Baby and Frog Baby met in the rain forest and played games all day. First, they played leap frog. Then they played hide and hug.

That night, Frog Baby told his mother about the games he played.

"No, no, Frog Baby! Hide and hug is not a game for you. It is the game of the hiss, coil, and squeeze. Promise you will never play with him again."

Snake Baby also told his mother about the games he played.

"No, no, Snake Baby! Hide and hug is not a game for you. Hide and hug is what you must do. This is the way you get your meals! Promise me you will hiss, coil, and squeeze."

Drawing Conclusions and Making Inferences

15. From the folktale, you can tell that

Ⓐ Snake Baby will eat Frog Baby.
Ⓑ Snake Baby will never hiss, coil, or squeeze again.
Ⓒ Frog Baby will still play safely with Snake Baby.
Ⓓ Frog Baby will be in danger if he plays with Snake Baby again.

Drawing Conclusions and Making Inferences

16. The folktale suggests that

Ⓐ frogs are smarter than snakes.
Ⓑ frogs are a danger to snakes.
Ⓒ snakes are supposed to eat frogs.
Ⓓ snakes are afraid of frogs.

Strategy Nine DISTINGUISHING BETWEEN FACT AND OPINION

PART ONE: Think About Fact and Opinion

What Is a Fact?

Have you ever told someone about what you were learning at school or what you had for dinner the night before? If so, you were telling facts. A fact tells about something that can be proved. If you say, "I learned about Johnny Appleseed in school," you are telling a fact.

★ Write one fact about your favorite TV show.

____

What Is an Opinion?

Have you ever told someone about things that you like? If so, you were telling opinions. An opinion tells about something you think or believe. An opinion cannot be proved. If you say, "I liked the book about Arthur and his friends," you are expressing an opinion.

★ Write one opinion about your favorite TV show.

____

★ Write how your fact is different from your opinion.

____

____

You just wrote about fact and opinion!

Take turns telling a fact about something, such as the planets or the weather. Then tell an opinion about the same thing.

How Do You Find Facts and Opinions?

ome reading passages contain details that tell facts. Some passages also contain details hat are opinions. Some passages contain both facts and opinions. You can tell the ifference between a fact and an opinion by asking yourself one question: "Does this etail tell about something that can be proved?" If your answer is "yes," then the detail a fact. If your answer is "no," then the detail is an opinion.

ead the passage below. See if you can tell the facts from the opinions.

> Today was the best day ever! I won a writing contest at school. I have never won anything before. I will always remember this day.

hink about what is a fact and what is an opinion.

et's find what can be proved and what cannot be proved.

ook at the chart below. Fill in the missing information.

Detail	Can this be proved?	Fact	Opinion
oday was the best day ever!	No		✔
won a writing contest at school.	Yes	✔	
have never won anything before.			
will always remember his day.			

> You found facts and opinions!

PART TWO: Learn About Distinguishing Between Fact and Opinion

Read this paragraph about San Francisco. As you read, look for statements that can be proved. Also look for statements that tell what someone thinks or feels.

San Francisco is located in California. I believe this city is the most beautiful city in the United States. The blue waters of the Pacific Ocean lie to the west. San Francisco Bay is to the east. The Golden Gate Bridge connects the city to northern California. San Francisco is the perfect spot for your next vacation!

The statements that can be proved are

San Francisco is located in California.
The blue waters of the Pacific Ocean lie to the west.
San Francisco Bay is to the east.
The Golden Gate Bridge connects the city to northern California.

The statements that tell what someone thinks or feels are

I believe this city is the most beautiful city in the United States.
San Francisco is the perfect spot for your next vacation!

If a statement can be proved, it is a **fact**. If a statement tells what someone thinks or feels about something, it is an **opinion**. Facts can be proved. Opinions cannot. When you figure out if a statement is a fact or an opinion, you are **distinguishing between fact and opinion**.

★ Facts are statements that can be checked or proved.

★ Opinions are statements that cannot be proved. They tell what someone thinks or feels.

★ Opinions often contain such clue words as *think, feel, believe,* and *seem.* Other common clue words are *always, never, all, none, most, least, greatest, best,* and *worst.*

Read this movie review written by a ten-year-old boy. As you read, ask yourself, "Which statements can be proved? Which statements cannot be proved?" Then answer the questions.

Badzilla

If you like scary movies, I think you will love the new movie *Badzilla*. If you don't like scary movies, stay home. *Badzilla* is not the movie for you. No movie ever made is scarier than *Badzilla*.

Badzilla is the name of the monster in the movie. Badzilla is half-robot and half-human. He was made by a scientist named Dr. Norma Tate. One day, Badzilla escapes from the lab where he was built. Dr. Tate sets off on a trip across the country to save her greatest creation.

Badzilla is now showing at Global Theater. It is also showing at Reed's Cinema downtown. If you can, see the movie at Global Theater. It's the best theater in town.

1. Which of these is a *fact*?

Ⓐ *Badzilla* is not the movie for you.

Ⓑ *Badzilla* is now showing at Global Theater.

Ⓒ No movie ever made is scarier than *Badzilla*.

Ⓓ If you like scary movies, I think you will love the new movie *Badzilla*.

2. Which clue word signals an *opinion* about Global Theater?

Ⓐ greatest

Ⓑ think

Ⓒ never

Ⓓ best

Talk about your answers to questions 1 and 2. Tell why you chose the answers you did.

PART THREE: Check Your Understanding

Remember: Facts can be proved, but opinions cannot be proved.

★ To find out if a statement is a fact, ask yourself, "Can this statement be proved?"

★ To find out if a statement is an opinion, ask yourself, "Does this statement tell what someone thinks or feels?"

★ Look for clue words that signal an opinion, such as *think, feel, believe, seem, always, never, all, none, most, least, greatest, best,* and *worst.*

Read this story about a boy who lives in Ghana. As you read, think about which statements are facts and which statements are opinions. Then answer the questions.

My name is Asare, and I am from Ghana. I think you do not know very much about Ghana, so I will tell you a little bit.

Ghana is a country on the west coast of Africa. I live with my family near the capital of Accra. My father is a fisherman. He says that fishing has changed a lot in the past years. When my great-grandfather was a fisherman, he carved his own boat out of wood. He sailed out to sea with many other men, each in his own canoe. Today, my father still fishes from a canoe. But his canoe has a motor. It is much better to have a boat with a motor.

In Ghana, many people fish in Lake Volta. Lake Volta is a very large lake in the eastern part of Ghana. But my father fishes in the Atlantic Ocean. When he catches tuna, I am the happiest boy in Ghana. Tuna is the most delicious fish!

3. Which of these statements tells what someone thinks or feels?

Ⓐ My name is Asare, and I am from Ghana.

Ⓑ In Ghana, many people fish in Lake Volta.

Ⓒ But my father fishes in the Atlantic Ocean.

Ⓓ Tuna is the most delicious fish!

4. Which of these statements can be proved?

Ⓐ I am the happiest boy in Ghana.

Ⓑ It is much better to have a boat with a motor.

Ⓒ Lake Volta is a very large lake in the eastern part of Ghana.

Ⓓ I think you do not know very much about Ghana.

Look at the answer choices for each question. Read why each answer choice is correct or not correct.

3. Which of these statements tells what someone thinks or feels?

Ⓐ My name is Asare, and I am from Ghana.

This answer is not correct because this statement is a fact. It can be proved that this is the boy's name and country.

Ⓑ In Ghana, many people fish in Lake Volta.

This answer is not correct because this statement is a fact. It can be proved, by watching or observing the lake, that many people fish there.

Ⓒ But my father fishes in the Atlantic Ocean.

This answer is not correct because this statement is a fact. It can be proved, by watching or observing Asare's father, that his father fishes in the Atlantic Ocean.

● Tuna is the most delicious fish!

This answer is correct because it tells how Asare feels about the taste of tuna. This statement cannot be proved.

4. Which of these statements can be proved?

Ⓐ I am the happiest boy in Ghana.

This answer is not correct because it cannot be proved that Asare is the happiest boy in Ghana. Most likely, other boys are as happy, or happier, than he at certain times.

Ⓑ It is much better to have a boat with a motor.

This answer is not correct because it cannot be proved. This statement tells how Asare feels about which kind of boat is better. Most likely, other people have different ideas about what kind of boat is better. The clue word better *signals that this statement is an opinion, not a fact.*

● Lake Volta is a very large lake in the eastern part of Ghana.

This answer is correct because it can be proved. You can find facts about Lake Volta in an encyclopedia or atlas.

Ⓓ I think you do not know very much about Ghana.

This answer is not correct because it cannot be proved. Asare has no idea how much the readers of his story know about Ghana. The clue word think *signals that this statement is an opinion, not a fact.*

PART FOUR: Learn More About Distinguishing Between Fact and Opinion

★ Facts can be checked or tested. You can prove that a fact is correct or true.

★ Opinions express someone's thoughts, feelings, or beliefs. An opinion can be about an event, an idea, a person, or a thing. Even if a person agrees or disagrees with an opinion, it still cannot be proved.

Read this article written about wind. Then answer the questions.

Wind is the most amazing force. Wind is something that you can't see, but you know when it is there. You can feel it. I love the feeling of wind blowing through my hair.

Wind is air that is moving. Sometimes, the air moves slowly, and there is a gentle breeze. Wind can also move quickly, causing strong winds. A strong wind can knock down a tree or a power line. The best wind is a gentle wind.

Besides speed, wind has direction. Winds are described by the direction from which they come. A north wind blows from the north to the south. A south wind blows from the south to the north.

Though you can't see wind, you can see what it does. Trees sway, windows rattle, and leaves are blown from their branches. There is nothing more fun than watching fall leaves whirling around like a tornado.

5. Which of these is a *fact* from the article?

Ⓐ Wind is air that is moving.
Ⓑ The best wind is a gentle wind.
Ⓒ Wind is the most amazing force.
Ⓓ There is nothing more fun than watching fall leaves whirling around like a tornado.

6. Which of these tells what someone thinks or feels?

Ⓐ A strong wind can knock down a tree or a power line.
Ⓑ Besides speed, wind has direction.
Ⓒ I love the feeling of wind blowing through my hair.
Ⓓ A south wind blows from the south to the north.

7. Which of these clue words signals an *opinion* about a gentle wind?

Ⓐ most
Ⓑ best
Ⓒ always
Ⓓ feel

8. Which of these can be proved?

Ⓐ Wind is the most amazing force.
Ⓑ The best wind is a gentle wind.
Ⓒ Wind is something that you can't see.
Ⓓ There is nothing more fun than watching fall leaves whirling around like a tornado.

Read this report written by a student. Then answer the questions.

I Want to Be a Veterinarian

I want to be a veterinarian when I grow up. Vets have the most interesting jobs. I think I would make a good vet. I love animals, and animals seem to love me. I am good at math and science. These skills will help me become the best vet ever.

Vets are like physicians. The only difference is that vets treat animals, not people. Vets do the same things that other doctors do. They treat illnesses, give medicine, and perform operations.

Most people think of a vet as a pet doctor who treats sick dogs and cats. Vets do more than help pets that are sick. Farmers depend on vets to keep their animals free of disease. An illness that spreads among farm animals can put a farmer out of business.

Vets also help keep zoo animals healthy. Some vets help preserve endangered animals. Other vets do research. There are many different types of work that a vet can do.

9. Which of these statements from the report can be proved?

Ⓐ I think I would make a good vet.

Ⓑ Most people think of a vet as a pet doctor who treats sick dogs and cats.

Ⓒ Vets do more than help pets that are sick.

Ⓓ I love animals, and animals seem to love me.

0. Which of these is a *fact* from the report?

Ⓐ Vets have the most interesting jobs.

Ⓑ Vets are like physicians.

Ⓒ I am good at math and science.

Ⓓ These skills will help me become the best vet ever.

11. Which statement is an *opinion*?

Ⓐ Farmers depend on vets to keep their animals free of disease.

Ⓑ Vets also help keep zoo animals healthy.

Ⓒ Other vets do research.

Ⓓ I think I would make a good vet.

12. Which of these tells what someone thinks or feels about vets?

Ⓐ Vets treat animals, not people.

Ⓑ Vets have the most interesting jobs.

Ⓒ Vets treat illnesses, perform operations, and give medicine.

Ⓓ Vets do more than help pets that are sick.

PART FIVE: Prepare for a Test

★ A test question about distinguishing between fact and opinion may ask you to identify which of four statements is a fact or an opinion.

★ To recognize a *fact*, read each answer choice and ask yourself, "Can this statement be proved?" If it can, then it is a fact.

★ To recognize an *opinion*, read each answer choice and ask yourself, "Does this statement tell what someone thinks or feels?" If it does, then it is an opinion. You can also look in the answer choices for clue words that signal an opinion.

Read this article about a popular kind of puzzle. Then answer questions about the article. Choose the best answer for Numbers 13 and 14.

People young and old never get tired of doing jigsaw puzzles. These puzzles have been around for hundreds of years. They get their name because of the kind of saw that is used to cut their unusual shapes—a jig saw.

Jigsaw puzzles were first made in England long ago. They were used to teach students about geography. They were made by first drawing a map on a sheet of wood. The wood was then cut with a jig saw into different shapes. Later, different kinds of pictures were made into puzzles. These pictures taught about history, the alphabet, plants, and animals. In time, the puzzles became more of a game than a learning tool.

Jigsaw puzzles became popular in the United States during the early 1930s. This was a time when people did not have much money. Jigsaw puzzles were a fun gift that didn't cost a lot of money. Today, putting these puzzles together is still the best way to pass the time without spending lots of money. Jigsaw puzzles will always be popular.

Distinguishing Between Fact and Opinion

13. Which of these is an *opinion* from the article?

Ⓐ Jigsaw puzzles were first made in England long ago.

Ⓑ These puzzles have been around for hundreds of years.

Ⓒ People young and old never get tired of doing jigsaw puzzles.

Ⓓ Jigsaw puzzles were first made in England long ago.

Distinguishing Between Fact and Opinion

14. Which of these is a *fact* about jigsaw puzzles?

Ⓐ Jigsaw puzzles will always be popular.

Ⓑ In time, the puzzles became more of a game than a learning tool.

Ⓒ Today, putting these puzzles together is still the best way to pass the time without spending lots of money.

Ⓓ People young and old never get tired of doing jigsaw puzzles.

Read this editorial that appeared in a student newspaper. Then answer questions about the article. Choose the best answer for Numbers 15 and 16.

Students Need Lunchtime Recess

Something must be done about the school lunchroom. For weeks, many students have been misbehaving at lunch. As a result, all students have lost their lunchtime recess. It's not fair that students who behave well are also getting punished. Students need recess. We are in our classrooms most of the day. We need to go outside and have some time to be free from our studies. We do have a ten-minute recess in the morning. But this is not enough.

Everyone agrees that students should not misbehave at lunch. But punishing all students is not the answer. The students who are causing the problem will never stop unless they are punished separately. Students and teachers must work together to solve this problem.

Distinguishing Between Fact and Opinion

15. Which of these is a *fact* from the article?
    - Ⓐ Students need recess.
    - Ⓑ But punishing all students is not the answer.
    - Ⓒ All students have lost their lunchtime recess.
    - Ⓓ Something must be done about the school lunchroom.

Distinguishing Between Fact and Opinion

16. Which of these tells what someone thinks or feels?
    - Ⓐ For weeks, many students have been misbehaving at lunch.
    - Ⓑ It's not fair that students who behave well are also getting punished.
    - Ⓒ We are in our classrooms most of the day.
    - Ⓓ We do have a ten-minute recess in the morning.

Strategies Seven–Nine REVIEW

PART ONE: Read a Biography

Read this short biography. Then answer questions about the biography. Choose the best answer for Numbers 1 through 6.

Marian Wright was born in South Carolina in 1939. She was the youngest of five children. Marian's parents believed that their children should always work hard. They did chores around the house. They had to spend one hour each night reading. They also helped people in their community.

As a child, Marian saw many examples of prejudice. Black children could not go to school with white children. Black children and white children could not play in the same playgrounds. Black people could not go to the best hospitals. Marian did not feel that this was fair or right.

Marian studied hard and went to college. After college, she went to law school to become a lawyer. In 1968, she married Peter Edelman.

As a lawyer, Marian worked to improve children's lives. Helping other people, especially children, is important work. Marian started the Children's Defense Fund. The Children's Defense Fund works to give all children in the United States the things they need to do well. Everyone should support the work of the Children's Defense Fund.

Marian Wright Edelman does not just look at a problem. She always works hard to find a solution. This remarkable woman is someone to be admired.

Finding Word Meaning in Context

1. In paragraph 2, the word *prejudice* means

Ⓐ "unfair treatment."
Ⓑ "kind actions."
Ⓒ "curious behavior."
Ⓓ "strange ideas."

Finding Word Meaning in Context

2. In the last paragraph, which group of words hints at the meaning of the word *solution*?

Ⓐ She always works hard . . .
Ⓑ . . . does not just look at a problem.
Ⓒ This remarkable woman . . .
Ⓓ . . . is someone to be admired.

Drawing Conclusions and Making Inferences

3. From this biography, you can tell that Marian Wright Edelman is

Ⓐ troubled about world peace.
Ⓑ interested mostly in herself.
Ⓒ concerned about people.
Ⓓ involved in her community.

Drawing Conclusions and Making Inferences

4. The biography suggests that Marian Wright Edelman's parents

Ⓐ rarely spent time with their children.
Ⓑ believed that reading was important.
Ⓒ didn't want Marian to attend law school.
Ⓓ thought that their daughter would not do much with her life.

Distinguishing Between Fact and Opinion

5. Which clue word signals an *opinion* of Marian's about what she saw as a child?

Ⓐ always
Ⓑ believe
Ⓒ all
Ⓓ feel

Distinguishing Between Fact and Opinion

6. Which of these is a *fact*?

Ⓐ Everyone should support the work of the Children's Defense Fund.
Ⓑ Marian started the Children's Defense Fund.
Ⓒ Helping other people, especially children, is important work.
Ⓓ This remarkable woman is someone to be admired.

PART TWO: Read a Folktale

Read this Chinese folktale. Then answer questions about the folktale. Choose the best answer for Numbers 7 through 12.

Like Master, Like Servant

One day in China, a man called Ping Sin decided to go out for a walk. Now, Ping Sin was the silliest man in China. Ping Sin was such a noodlehead that when he put on his boots, he never noticed that they were two different boots. One boot had a thick sole, and the other had a thin sole.

Ping Sin set off on his walk. His servant, Pu Shih, followed behind him. Ping Sin soon found it difficult to walk. One foot was always sinking more deeply than the other.

A stranger passed by and saw the trouble Ping Sin was having.

"Excuse me," the stranger said, smiling. "You are having trouble walking because one of your boots has a thick sole and the other has a thin one. Put on two boots with the same kinds of soles, and you will have no more trouble walking."

Ping Sin turned to his servant and said, "Pu Shih, return to the house and bring me my other boots."

The servant ran back to the house and quickly found the other boots. He looked at them carefully. One boot had a thick sole, and the other had a thin sole.

"These are no better than the boots my master has on now. There's no reason to bring these to him. They are as uneven as the boots he is wearing."

Pu Shih ran back to his master, who was waiting for him. When Ping Sin saw him return empty-handed, he asked, "Where are the boots I asked you for?"

"Master," Pu Shih said, "the boots at home also had one thick sole and one thin sole. They are no better than the ones you are wearing."

What do you think Ping Sin said to Pu Shih?

"How fortunate I am to have such a wise servant," said Ping Sin. "Today, my walk must be a hard one." And the two men continued down the road.

Finding Word Meaning in Context

7. You can tell that a noodlehead is someone who
   - Ⓐ is silly.
   - Ⓑ likes macaroni.
   - Ⓒ is intelligent.
   - Ⓓ lived long ago.

Finding Word Meaning in Context

8. In the last paragraph, the word *fortunate* means
   - Ⓐ "unhappy."
   - Ⓑ "foolish."
   - Ⓒ "clever."
   - Ⓓ "lucky."

Drawing Conclusions and Making Inferences

9. Ping Sin wasn't angry at Pu Shih for not bringing back his boots because Ping Sin
   - Ⓐ saw that his servant was already upset.
   - Ⓑ was always patient with his servant.
   - Ⓒ didn't really want to change his boots.
   - Ⓓ was as foolish as his servant.

Drawing Conclusions and Making Inferences

10. Which detail from the folktale helped you answer question 9?
   - Ⓐ "How fortunate I am to have such a wise servant," said Ping Sin.
   - Ⓑ "They are no better than the ones you are wearing."
   - Ⓒ "Pu Shih, return to the house and bring me my other boots."
   - Ⓓ "You are having trouble walking because one of your boots has a thick sole and the other has a thin one."

Distinguishing Between Fact and Opinion

11. Which of these is a *fact*?
   - Ⓐ Ping Sin was the best master.
   - Ⓑ Ping Sin was the wisest of men.
   - Ⓒ Ping Sin sent his servant back to the house.
   - Ⓓ Ping Sin was the silliest man in China.

Distinguishing Between Fact and Opinion

12. Which of these tells an *opinion*?
   - Ⓐ "How fortunate I am to have such a wise servant."
   - Ⓑ "You are having trouble walking because one of your boots has a thick sole and the other has a thin one."
   - Ⓒ "They are as uneven as the boots he is wearing."
   - Ⓓ "Pu Shih, return to the house and bring me my other boots."

Strategy Ten IDENTIFYING AUTHOR'S PURPOSE

PART ONE: Think About Author's Purpose

WHAT IS AUTHOR'S PURPOSE?

Authors always write for a reason. Everything you read has a purpose.
The author's purpose is either to describe, to entertain, to explain, or to persuade.

★ Write what you think the author's purpose is for writing each of the following. Tell if the author's purpose is to describe, to entertain, to explain, or to persuade.

A newspaper article

The author's purpose is to ____ .

A comic book

The author's purpose is to ____ .

An advertisement

The author's purpose is to ____ .

A paragraph about what owls look like

The author's purpose is to ____ .

You just wrote about author's purpose!

Take turns talking about some of the different things you have read. Think about things such as books, newspaper ads, movie reviews, and poems. Together, see if you can identify the author's purpose for what you read.

How Do You Find Author's Purpose?

Every reading passage is written for a reason. When you read, ask yourself, "What does the author want me to know?" Your answer will help you figure out the author's purpose. Read the passage below. See if you can figure out the author's purpose.

> I named my pet hamster Peaches because she is orange and white. Peaches has black eyes that look like tiny beads. Sometimes she keeps food in her cheeks. This makes her face puff out. Peaches looks funny with her huge cheeks and small body.

Think about what the author wants you to know.

Let's find the author's purpose.

First, let's narrow down the choices in the chart below.

Check "yes" or "no" for each choice. You can check "yes" only once.

What does the passage do?	Yes	No	If "yes", then
Does the passage mostly try to make you laugh or teach an important lesson?			the author's purpose is to entertain.
Does the passage mostly tell how to do or make something?			the author's purpose is to explain.
Does the passage mostly try to get you to do or buy something?			the author's purpose is to persuade.
Does the passage mostly give details about a particular person, place, or thing?			the author's purpose is to describe.

★ Write the choice that has a check mark next to "yes."

____

> You just found the author's purpose!

PART TWO: Learn About Identifying Author's Purpose

Read this poem about a dinner invitation. As you read, think about why the author probably wrote the poem.

Would you like to come for dinner?

We're having strawberry jelly and pork belly,
Cold potatoes and fried tomatoes,
Jars of jam and chops of lamb,
Legs of frogs and chili dogs.
For dessert we'll have some custard.
I like mine with a dab of mustard.

Would you like to come for dinner?

The author probably wrote the poem to make you smile or laugh. The author's purpose is to entertain readers with a silly poem.

All authors write for a reason. The reason an author writes something is called the author's purpose. When you figure out why a reading passage was written, you are **identifying the author's purpose**. Authors write for one of four reasons—to describe, to entertain, to explain, or to persuade.

★ Some reading passages mainly describe something, such as a person, place, or thing. The author's purpose is to **describe**.

★ Some reading passages mainly tell a personal story, tell something funny, or use a story to teach a lesson. The author's purpose is to **entertain**.

★ Some reading passages mainly tell how to do something, or contain lots of information about a person, place, or thing. The author's purpose is to **explain**.

★ Some reading passages are mainly written to try to get readers to do something, buy something, or believe something. The author's purpose is to **persuade**.

Read this ad for a pizza shop. As you read, try to figure out the author's purpose for writing the ad. Then answer the questions.

LENA'S PIZZA

The Best Pizza You'll Ever Eat!

People in Chicago say Chicago has the most delicious pizza. In Los Angeles, people say Los Angeles has the best pizza in the world. For New Yorkers, only New York-style pizza will do. Others say that you have to go to Italy to taste real pizza.

Now you don't have to go to Chicago, Los Angeles, New York, or Italy, to get delicious pizza. You can get the world's best pizza right here in Springfield at Lena's.

Lena has just returned from a trip around the world. She went in search of delicious pizza. She tasted all the pizza she could find. She learned the secrets of the world's best pizza makers. Now Lena has returned to Springfield. Come to Lena's Pizza! Let Lena make the world's best pizza for you!

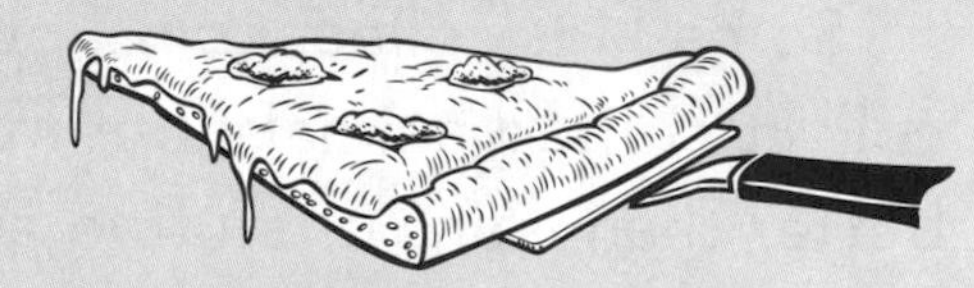

Lena's Pizza • 1492 North Main Street • Springfield

1. The author wrote the ad mainly to
   - Ⓐ explain the history of pizza.
   - Ⓑ describe pizza to people who have never seen it.
   - Ⓒ entertain readers with a funny story.
   - Ⓓ get readers to try Lena's pizza.

2. You know your answer to question 1 is correct because the ad mainly
   - Ⓐ contains many details that describe something.
   - Ⓑ provides facts or tells readers how to do something.
   - Ⓒ tries to convince readers of something.
   - Ⓓ tells an enjoyable story.

Talk about your answers to questions 1 and 2. Tell why you chose the answers you did.

PART THREE: Check Your Understanding

Remember: Authors write to describe, to entertain, to explain, or to persuade.

★ To figure out if the author's purpose is to describe, ask yourself, "Does the author provide lots of details about a particular person, place, or thing?"

★ To figure out if the author's purpose is to entertain, ask yourself, "Does the author tell a personal story or try to make me laugh? Does the author use a story to teach a lesson?"

★ To figure out if the author's purpose is to explain, ask yourself, "Does the author tell me facts about a person, place, or thing? Does the author tell me how to do or make something?"

★ To figure out if the author's purpose is to persuade, ask yourself, "Does the author try to get me to do something, buy something, or believe something?"

Read this passage about an unusual collection. As you read, ask yourself, "Why did the author probably write this passage?" Then answer the questions.

Some kids collect coins, but I can't keep a quarter without spending it. Some kids collect stuffed animals, but my room is the size of a closet. Me, I collect something better than coins or stuffed animals.

I collect pencils. That's right—pencils. Short ones, tall ones, red ones, blue ones, and, of course, yellow ones. I have one shoe box full of just different kinds of yellow pencils. So far, I have over 1,000 pencils.

If you don't have a lot of money or a lot of space, you might want to start a pencil collection of your own. Pencils aren't expensive. They don't take up a lot of room. And when someone in your class says, "Hey, anyone got an extra pencil?" well, you'll know what to say!

3. The author wrote the passage mainly to
- Ⓐ entertain readers with a story about a pencil collection.
- Ⓑ explain how to start a coin collection.
- Ⓒ make readers believe that pencil collections are better than other collections.
- Ⓓ describe the kind of pencils he collects.

4. You know your answer to question 3 is correct because the passage mainly
- Ⓐ contains many details that describe something.
- Ⓑ provides facts or tells readers how to do something.
- Ⓒ tries to convince readers of something.
- Ⓓ tells an enjoyable story.

Look at the answer choices for each question. Read why each answer choice is correct or not correct.

3. The author wrote the passage mainly to

● entertain readers with a story about a pencil collection.

This answer is correct because the passage mainly tells a personal story that is enjoyable to read.

Ⓑ explain how to start a coin collection.

This answer is not correct because the passage does not contain information that explains how to start a coin collection. The author mentions only that some people collect coins, not how to start a coin collection.

Ⓒ make readers believe that pencil collections are better than other collections.

This answer is not correct because the passage does not contain opinions about one kind of collection being better than another kind of collection.

Ⓓ describe the kind of pencils he collects.

This answer is not correct because the passage does not mainly provide lots of details about the kinds of pencils the author collects.

4. You know your answer to question 3 is correct because the passage mainly

Ⓐ contains many details that describe something.

This answer is not correct because the passage does not contain lots of details that describe a particular person, place, or thing. The passage does provide some descriptions about the pencils in the author's collection, but this is not the main purpose of the passage.

Ⓑ provides facts or tells readers how to do something.

This answer is not correct because the passage does not mainly contain facts or information that teaches or explains how to do something.

Ⓒ tries to convince readers of something.

This answer is not correct because the passage does not mainly contain opinions that try to get readers to do, buy, or believe something.

● tells an enjoyable story.

This answer is correct because the passage tells a personal story about something the author finds fun to do.

PART FOUR: Learn More About Identifying Author's Purpose

Different reading passages are written for different purposes. Knowing the kind of passage you are reading often helps you identify the author's purpose.

★ Articles are usually written to describe or explain. Some articles describe a person, place, or thing. Others explain something, such as the cause of pollution.

★ Directions are written to explain.

★ Personal stories, riddles, and poetry are written to entertain.

★ Ads and articles in which an opinion is stated are written to persuade.

Read each passage. Then answer the questions.

I **The Bird House**
28 Main St., Groton

We have the largest selection of birdseed, birdbaths, and feeders in town. We also have the lowest prices! You won't find a better deal anywhere! Come see us today!

II **My Window**

I have a bird feeder on the outside of my window. One day, a little bird was trying to eat, but a bigger bird kept chasing him away. I was worried about the little bird. So I got an idea. I put a picture of my cat on the window. The next time the big bird came by, he flew away. And he's never come back!

III **Easy Bird Feeder**

First, find a large pinecone. Then fill all the open spaces with peanut butter. Next, roll the pinecone in birdseed. Add a string to hang your bird feeder from a tree. Now sit back and wait for the birds to arrive!

IV **The Cardinal**

The cardinal is a bird that is enjoyed by many bird-watchers. The cardinal is found in the eastern United States. It is also found in parts of Mexico and California. The male is bright red with a black throat. The female is mostly brown, with red on its wings and tail. Both birds have a red cluster of feathers on their head.

5. The author's main purpose in passage I is to
Ⓐ describe. Ⓒ entertain.
Ⓑ explain. Ⓓ persuade.

6. The author's main purpose in passage II is to
Ⓐ describe. Ⓒ entertain.
Ⓑ explain. Ⓓ persuade.

7. The author's main purpose in passage III is to
Ⓐ describe. Ⓒ entertain.
Ⓑ explain. Ⓓ persuade.

8. The author's main purpose in passage IV is to
Ⓐ describe. Ⓒ entertain.
Ⓑ explain. Ⓓ persuade.

Read this fable about two frogs. Then answer the questions.

The Frogs and the Well

There were once two frogs that lived together in a marsh. The marsh was a wonderful place for frogs. Frogs like wet, damp places. There were always lots of bugs to eat and there was always lots of water to drink.

One hot summer day, the marsh dried up. Now the marsh was as dry as a desert. The two frogs decided to find a new place to live.

After a while, the two frogs came to a deep well. One of the frogs looked down into the well and saw water. He said to his friend, "This looks like a nice, cool place. Let us jump in and settle here."

The other frog had a much wiser head on his shoulders. He replied, "Not so fast, my friend. What if the well dries up one day? How could we possibly get out of the well?"

The moral of the fable: *Look before you leap.*

9. The author wrote the first paragraph mainly to

Ⓐ explain why the frogs lived in a marsh.

Ⓑ try to get readers to learn about a marsh.

Ⓒ describe the marsh where the frogs lived.

Ⓓ entertain readers with a funny joke about a marsh.

10. The author wrote paragraph 2 mainly to

Ⓐ entertain readers with a story about frogs.

Ⓑ explain why the frogs had to move.

Ⓒ describe how the marsh dried up.

Ⓓ persuade readers to feel sorry for the frogs.

11. The author wrote paragraph 3 mainly to

Ⓐ describe the place where one frog wanted to settle.

Ⓑ explain why the frogs were looking for a new home.

Ⓒ persuade readers to learn more about deep wells.

Ⓓ entertain readers with a silly story about a frog.

12. The fable was written mainly to

Ⓐ explain why frogs don't live in wells.

Ⓑ persuade readers to avoid wells.

Ⓒ entertain readers with a story that teaches a lesson.

Ⓓ describe what a well looks like.

PART FIVE: Prepare for a Test

★ A test question about identifying the author's purpose may ask you why an author probably wrote a particular reading passage. This kind of question is asking about the purpose of the entire reading passage.

★ A test question about identifying the author's purpose may ask you why a particular paragraph was written. This kind of question is asking about only one part of the reading passage.

Read the instructions for making something for a room in your house. Then answer questions about the instructions. Choose the best answer for Numbers 13 and 14.

Some people separate the rooms in their home with strands of beads. The beads hang from the top of the door opening to the bottom of the floor. They click and clack whenever people go in and out of the room. You can make a curtain like this using macaroni and just a few beads.

Materials: several boxes of tube-shaped macaroni, strong cord, string, about thirty beads with an opening large enough to thread the string through, scissors

1. Measure the width of the door opening where your curtain will hang. Add about 4 inches to this measurement. Then cut the cord to this length.
2. Cut about thirty pieces of string. Cut them into whatever length you want your curtain to be. You might want the strands to hang from the top of the door opening to the floor. You might also want to have strands of different lengths.
3. Tie a bead to the end of each length of string. This will keep the macaroni from sliding off the string once you begin adding it.
4. Add pieces of macaroni to the string until you've covered up most of the string. Leave about three inches of string empty at the top. You'll need room to tie the finished strand to the cord.
5. Once you've filled enough strands and tied them to the cord, your curtain is ready to hang. Have an adult help you. You can use duct tape to hang your curtain. You can also make a loop at each end of the cord. Hammer a nail into each end of the door opening and attach a loop to each nail.

Identifying Author's Purpose

13. The author wrote the first paragraph mainly to

Ⓐ persuade readers to make a curtain.
Ⓑ describe a kind of curtain used by some people.
Ⓒ explain how to make a curtain.
Ⓓ entertain readers with a funny story.

Identifying Author's Purpose

14. The instructions were written mainly to

Ⓐ explain how to make something.
Ⓑ describe something about other people's homes.
Ⓒ get readers to make a curtain for their room.
Ⓓ entertain readers with an article about macaroni.

Read this article about a unique invention. Then answer questions about the article. Choose the best answer for Numbers 15 and 16.

In the early 1940s, James Wright created a new type of rubber for a company named General Electric. His invention could bounce higher than a rubber ball and could lift ink off a newspaper page. However, General Electric did not have any practical uses for this new rubber. The company mailed samples of the new rubber to several people to see if they could find a good use for it.

Some time later, a toy-store worker named Paul Hodgson saw a group of adults playing with this rubber. He was surprised at how much fun they were having. Hodgson wrote to General Electric and asked if he could sell the rubber. In 1949, he began to sell the rubber in packages shaped like eggs. Hodgson called it Silly Putty®. Silly Putty® became a huge success. At long last, a use for the new rubber had been found.

Identifying Author's Purpose

15. The author wrote the first paragraph mainly to

Ⓐ describe a new kind of rubber that was invented.

Ⓑ explain how rubber is made.

Ⓒ try to get readers to try out their own inventions.

Ⓓ entertain readers with a story about silly inventions.

Identifying Author's Purpose

16. The article was written mainly to

Ⓐ persuade readers to buy Silly Putty®.

Ⓑ describe how Silly Putty® works.

Ⓒ explain how a popular toy was invented.

Ⓓ entertain readers with a story about Silly Putty®.

Strategy Eleven INTERPRETING FIGURATIVE LANGUAGE

PART ONE: Think About Figurative Language

WHAT IS FIGURATIVE LANGUAGE?

Has the cat ever got your tongue? If so, you were not very talkative. What about getting up on the wrong side of the bed? If you did, then you were in a bad mood. Figurative language is the use of words in a way that is different from what they usually mean.

★ Read this sentence.

I didn't mean to tell everyone about the surprise.

★ Now read the next sentence. It uses different words, but has the same meaning as the first sentence.

I didn't mean to spill the beans about the surprise.

★ Write which sentence is more interesting, the first one or the second one. Tell why you chose the sentence you did.

____

____

____

You just wrote about figurative language!

Talk about some of the words you have used or heard that have a meaning different from their usual meaning. You might have heard someone say that he "feels like a million dollars" when he feels great. See how many examples of figurative language you can think of.

How Do You Understand Figurative Language?

Sometimes you can use word meaning in context to help you understand figurative language. Look for clues in a reading passage to help you figure out what new meaning the words could have. Clues might be in the sentence where the words are found. They may also be in the sentence just before or just after the one where the words are found. Read the passage below. See if you can figure out what the words *all thumbs* mean.

> My neighbor, Mrs. Gomez, asked me to help her fix her bird feeder. "It should be easy to fix with a nail or two. But I'm all thumbs with a hammer," she said. "I might hit my fingers by mistake."

Think about what the words *all thumbs* mean.

Let's find word meaning in context.

First, let's narrow down the clues.

The chart below shows three sentences: the one that comes before the words *all thumbs*, the one that contains the words *all thumbs*, and the one that comes after the words *all thumbs*.

Look carefully at the sentences that come before and after the words *all thumbs*.

"It should be easy to fix with a nail or two."	"But I am all thumbs with a hammer."	"I might hit my fingers by mistake."
Before		After

Now think about what the clues in the sentences tell you:

The bird feeder should be easy to fix.
But Mrs. Gomez still wants someone to help her.
She thinks she might hit her fingers by mistake.

So, the words *all thumbs* must mean ______________________________________.

> You just worked with figurative language!

PART TWO: Learn About Interpreting Figurative Language

Read this sentence. As you read, think about the two things being compared.

The tornado was as fierce as a *T. Rex*.

The two things being compared are a tornado and a *T. Rex*.
The writer used a **simile** to help readers picture how terrible the tornado was.
A simile uses the word *like* or *as* to compare two different things.

Read this sentence. As you read, think about the two things being compared.

Ned's legs were shaking leaves.

The two things being compared are Ned's legs and shaking leaves.
The writer used a **metaphor** to help readers picture how nervous Ned was.
A metaphor compares two different things but does not use the word *like* or *as*.
A metaphor says that one thing is another thing.

Now read this sentence. As you read, think about the meaning of the underlined words.

The dog <u>turned up her nose</u> at the food.

The underlined words mean that the dog did not care for the food.
The underlined words are an **idiom**.
An idiom is a group of words that have a meaning different from their usual meaning.

Similes, metaphors, and idioms are types of figurative language. Authors use figurative language to help readers create pictures in their mind. When you understand the meaning of a simile, a metaphor, or an idiom, you are **interpreting figurative language**.

★ Look for things that are compared in a reading passage. Try to find examples of similes or metaphors.

★ Look for phrases whose words have a meaning different from their usual meaning. Try to find examples of idioms.

★ Figurative language usually brings a picture to a reader's mind. Use that picture to help you understand the meaning of the figurative language.

Read this article about the athlete Mia Hamm. As you read, look for things that are compared. Also look for words that have a meaning different from their usual meaning. Then answer the questions.

Many soccer fans believe that Mia Hamm is the best female soccer player in the world. She has the speed of a cheetah. She can also stop and change direction as quick as a fox. These are important skills for a soccer player.

Mia played on the United States Olympic soccer team in 1996. The U.S. women's team beat China to win a gold medal. For Mia, it was a victory for all female athletes.

What does a new sports star do after winning a gold medal? Mia and her sister visited New York City for a little fun. They said they were going to have a ball.

1. In the article, Mia's speed is compared to the speed of

Ⓐ a sports star.

Ⓑ a fox.

Ⓒ a soccer player.

Ⓓ a cheetah.

2. In the last paragraph, what do the words *have a ball* mean?

Ⓐ "play soccer"

Ⓑ "enjoy themselves"

Ⓒ "take a tour"

Ⓓ "act foolishly"

Talk about your answers to questions 1 and 2. Tell why you chose the answers you did.

PART THREE: Check Your Understanding

Remember: Similes, metaphors, and idioms are types of figurative language. Authors use figurative language to help readers create pictures in their mind.

★ Look for things that are compared in a reading passage.

★ Look for phrases whose words have a meaning different from their usual meaning.

★ Think about any pictures that come to mind as you read. Use those pictures to help you understand what is being described.

Read this article about a famous painting. As you read, ask yourself, "What pictures come to mind?" Then answer the questions.

Have you seen this painting before? This is a famous painting by the American artist Grant Wood. The painting is called *American Gothic.*

Grant Wood painted *American Gothic* in 1930. The painting was an overnight success. Wood was glad that so many people enjoyed his painting. He wanted everyday people, not just other artists, to enjoy his paintings.

Most people liked the way the man and woman in the painting looked. They appeared to be serious and hardworking. Many people thought that the couple looked the way all Americans should look. Others thought the couple looked as stiff as tree trunks.

Today, we see copies of Wood's painting in cartoons and advertisements. Sometimes, the faces of the man and woman are changed. They are replaced with the faces of famous people, like movie stars or other people in the news. Sometimes, the man and woman are put in a new setting. Keep your eye out for these two. You never know where they might turn up.

3. In paragraph 2, the words *overnight success* mean

Ⓐ "liked by only a few people."

Ⓑ "viewed at night."

Ⓒ "became popular right away."

Ⓓ "took a long time to become known."

4. The couple in the painting is compared to

Ⓐ a cartoon.

Ⓑ movie stars.

Ⓒ a painting.

Ⓓ tree trunks.

Look at the answer choices for each question. Read why each answer choice is correct or not correct.

3. In paragraph 2, the words *overnight success* mean

Ⓐ "liked by only a few people."

This answer is not correct because there are no details in the article to hint that only a few people liked the painting. In fact, the article states that "Most people liked the way the man and woman in the painting looked."

Ⓑ "viewed at night."

This answer is not correct because there are no details in the article to hint that the painting was seen at night.

● "became popular right away."

This answer is correct because details in the article hint that the painting became liked by many people rather quickly. The article states that "Wood was glad that so many people enjoyed his painting."

Ⓓ "took a long time to become known."

This answer is not correct because there are no details in the article to hint that the painting took a long time to be known by others.

4. The couple in the painting is compared to

Ⓐ a cartoon.

This answer is not correct because there is no comparison made between the couple and a cartoon. In paragraph 4, the article states that the couple sometimes appears in cartoons, but this is not a comparison.

Ⓑ movie stars.

This answer is not correct because there is no comparison made between the couple and a movie star. In paragraph 4, the article states that the faces of the couple are sometimes replaced with the faces of movie stars, but this is not a comparison.

Ⓒ a painting.

This answer is not correct because there is no comparison made between the couple and a painting. The article states that the couple appears in a famous painting, but this is not a comparison.

● tree trunks.

This answer is correct because in paragraph 3, the article states that "Others thought the couple looked as stiff as tree trunks." *The word* as *signals that two things are being compared in a simile.*

PART FOUR: Learn More About Interpreting Figurative Language

★ Think about the things being compared in a simile or a metaphor. Ask yourself, "What do the two things have in common?" This will help you create pictures in your mind.

★ Look at the sentences near an idiom. Look for context clues to help you figure out its meaning.

Read this tall tale about Paul Bunyan. Then answer the questions.

Paul Bunyan is the hero of many tall tales. There are more stories about Paul Bunyan than there are trees in a forest. Most of the stories tell about the amazing things that Paul did.

No one seems to know exactly when Paul was born. Most folks, however, agree that he was the biggest, strongest baby anyone had ever seen. As a baby, he was as large as a horse, and just as hungry. He wrestled bears for fun. Paul's favorite playmate was a big blue ox named Babe.

Paul was a lumberjack. He became famous for chopping down the forests that once covered America. Working like busy beavers, Paul and Babe cleared the land for farms and settlers. After one day of very hard work, Paul and Babe were thirsty. So they dug themselves the Great Lakes so that they would always have plenty of water to drink.

After Paul and Babe had cleared enough land for the settlers' farms, they went to Canada. From there, they decided to head out for Alaska. Just where they are today, no one is quite sure.

5. In paragraph 2, Paul's size is compared to that of

Ⓐ an ox.
Ⓑ a tree.
Ⓒ a horse.
Ⓓ a forest.

6. The sentence *There are more stories about Paul than there are trees in a forest* means that there are

Ⓐ few stories about Paul.
Ⓑ a lot of stories about Paul.
Ⓒ stories about Paul that are hard to believe.
Ⓓ stories about Paul that always take place in a forest.

7. The tall tale says that Paul and Babe worked like busy beavers. This means that they worked

Ⓐ in ponds.
Ⓑ slowly.
Ⓒ like farmers.
Ⓓ hard and long.

8. In the last paragraph, the words *head out* means

Ⓐ "live in."
Ⓑ "travel toward."
Ⓒ "travel away from."
Ⓓ "plan a trip."

Read this article about a World Cup soccer game. Then answer the questions.

In July 1998, France and Brazil faced each other for soccer's highest honor, the World Cup. The World Cup is to soccer what the World Series is to baseball.

Some people thought the French team didn't stand a chance against Brazil. Brazil was the better team, they said. Brazil had Ronaldo. Ronaldo has been called the world's best soccer player. Some have said that Ronaldo was a tiger on the field.

But France had Zinedine Ziane, the French magician. Ziane was an excellent player, but he did not often score goals. In the game against Brazil, Ziane scored two goals. "I was so hungry to score a World Cup goal that I made it two," he said. The final score was 3–0. France was the new world champion!

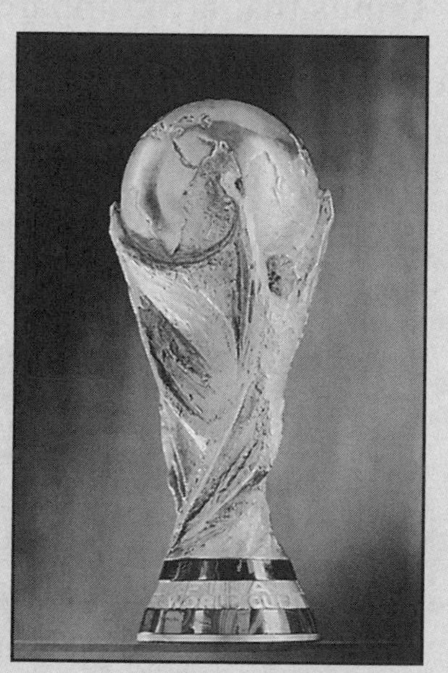
World Cup

9. In the article, the World Cup is compared to

Ⓐ a soccer game.
Ⓑ a high honor.
Ⓒ a baseball game.
Ⓓ the World Series.

10. Which two things are compared in the last paragraph?

Ⓐ a soccer game and a magic trick
Ⓑ a champion and a country
Ⓒ a soccer player and a magician
Ⓓ a soccer team and a goal

11. The words *didn't stand a chance* mean that the French team

Ⓐ was expected to win easily.
Ⓑ probably wouldn't play well.
Ⓒ didn't have much hope of winning.
Ⓓ had few players who could score.

12. Which of these is a metaphor?

Ⓐ Ronaldo was a tiger on the field.
Ⓑ Brazil was the better team.
Ⓒ Ziane scored two goals.
Ⓓ I was so hungry to score a World Cup goal.

PART FIVE: Prepare for a Test

★ A test question about interpreting figurative language may ask you about the meaning of a simile, a metaphor, or an idiom.

★ A test question about interpreting figurative language may ask you about things that are compared in the reading passage.

Read this story about a boy's visit to a museum. Then answer questions about the story. Choose the best answer for Numbers 13 and 14.

Roberto had just entered the museum with his parents. This was his first trip to the museum, but he wasn't very happy. His friends from school told him that a visit to the museum was about as much fun as cleaning your room.

As Roberto walked in the museum, he saw old airplanes and space rockets. He saw an enormous skeleton of a brontosaurus towering high above a group of gathering children. Roberto even saw a woman showing a group of children how a light bulb works. Roberto quickly became excited. "My friends must be pulling my leg!" thought Roberto. "Museums have all sorts of fun things." Roberto knew that his first trip to the museum certainly wouldn't be his last.

Interpreting Figurative Language

13. In the story, a visit to the museum is compared to

Ⓐ going to school.
Ⓑ looking at old airplanes.
Ⓒ cleaning one's room.
Ⓓ flying a rocket.

Interpreting Figurative Language

14. The words *pulling my leg* mean that Roberto thinks his friends are

Ⓐ harming him.
Ⓑ fooling him.
Ⓒ helping him.
Ⓓ pushing him.

Read this article about the first space-shuttle mission. Then answer questions about the article. Choose the best answer for Numbers 15 and 16.

On April 12, 1981, the space shuttle *Columbia* lifted off from Cape Canaveral, Florida. Captain John Young and Commander Robert Crippen were chosen to pilot this first space-shuttle flight. Their mission was to prove that a shuttle could work in space, and that it could be used for more than one mission.

Scientists had never tested the shuttle in space before. They were nervous during the launch. Scientists watched like hawks as the *Columbia* left the ground.

Young and Crippen spent two days in space. In that time, they were able to prove what scientists had hoped for. When the mission was completed on April 14, *Columbia* landed safely in California. Scientists were excited to find that their years of hard work were about to pay off.

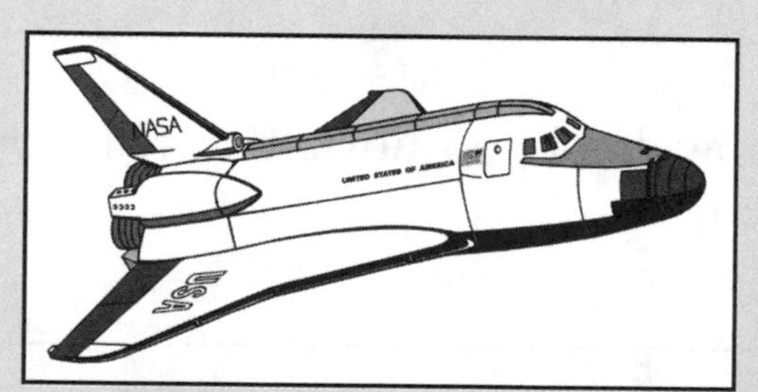

Space Shuttle *Columbia*

Interpreting Figurative Language

15. The words *watched liked hawks* mean that the scientists watched

Ⓐ slowly.
Ⓑ happily.
Ⓒ carefully.
Ⓓ while flying.

Interpreting Figurative Language

16. In the last sentence, the words *pay off* mean

Ⓐ "bring success."
Ⓑ "cause failure."
Ⓒ "receive money."
Ⓓ "cause injury."

Strategy Twelve DISTINGUISHING BETWEEN REAL AND MAKE-BELIEVE

PART ONE: Think About Real and Make-believe

WHAT IS REAL AND MAKE-BELIEVE?

Things that could really happen are real. Things that could not really happen are make-believe. Lots of books and movies are filled with things that could not really happen. Tiny people do not really live under the stairs and pigs cannot really build houses of wood, straw, or brick.

★ Write the name of a TV show, book, or movie that tells about something that could really happen.

____

★ What kinds of things could really happen?

____

____

★ Write the name of a TV show, book, or movie that tells about something that could not really happen.

____

★ What kinds of things could not really happen?

____

____

You just wrote about real and make-believe!

Take turns talking about things that could really happen and things that could not really happen. You can think about books you have read or movies you have seen, or you can use your imagination to think of your own ideas.

How Do You Tell the Difference Between Real and Make-believe?

Sometimes you can tell if what you are reading is real or make-believe by figuring out what you are reading. If you are reading a newspaper article or a biography, you know the things that happen are real. If you are reading a tall tale or a folktale, you know that many things that happen are make-believe. Read the passage below. See if you can figure out which things could really happen and which things could not.

> A wolf was walking through the woods. He stopped at a river for a drink. He saw his face reflected in the water. "I have never seen my own face," said the wolf. "What a handsome fellow I am." And he skipped and danced all the way home.

Think about what could really happen and what could not.

Let's find what is real and what is make-believe.

First, let's narrow down the clues.

The chart below shows the things the wolf does in the story. Tell if these things could really happen or could not really happen. The first one has been done for you.

Things the wolf does	Could really happen	Could not really happen
A wolf walks through the woods.	✔	
A wolf drinks out of a river.		
A wolf sees his own reflection in the water.		
A wolf talks.		
A wolf skips and dances.		

You just found the difference between real and make-believe!

PART TWO: Learn About Distinguishing Between Real and Make-believe

Read this story about an unusual dog. As you read, think about the things that could really happen and the things that could not really happen.

Rusty had woken up when the first glimmer of sun appeared. He spent the day exploring the countryside.

Rusty was ready to go home. He ran up to a yellow cab. The shaggy dog opened the door and jumped in. Rusty told the driver to take him home.

The things that could really happen

Rusty had woken up when the first glimmer of sun appeared.

He spent the day exploring the countryside.

Rusty was ready to go home.

He ran up to a yellow cab.

The things that could not really happen

The shaggy dog opened the door and jumped in.

Rusty told the driver to take him home.

Things you read that could happen in real life are **real**. Things you read that could not happen in real life are **make-believe**. When you figure out which parts of a reading passage are real and which parts are make-believe, you are **distinguishing between real and make-believe**.

★ Real stories are about events that could really happen.

★ Make-believe stories are about events that could not really happen. Clues that signal a story is make-believe are unlikely or magical events, imaginary places, talking animals, and characters who do impossible things.

★ Often, some parts of a story are real, and other parts are make-believe.

Read this story about a girl named Angela. As you read, think about which things in the story could really happen and which things could not really happen. Then answer the questions.

Angela never has to be woken up on Saturdays. On Saturday mornings, Angela jumps out of bed. Saturday is ballet day. Angela can't wait to get to class.

Right after breakfast, Angela gets ready to go to the ballet studio. She pulls her hair back into a bun. She stuffs her ballet shoes into her bag.

As her mother drives her to class, Angela begins to daydream. She sees herself on the center of a stage. She is wearing a glittering costume. On her feet are her magic dance shoes. Angela's feet begin to move as her magic shoes take over. She performs her routine beautifully. The audience cheers as Angela takes a bow.

1. Which of these could not really happen?
   - Ⓐ Angela jumps out of bed.
   - Ⓑ Angela gets ready for ballet class.
   - Ⓒ Angela wears a glittering costume.
   - Ⓓ Angela puts on her magic dance shoes.

2. How do you know that this story is mostly real?
   - Ⓐ Many dancers have magic ballet shoes.
   - Ⓑ People can really take ballet lessons.
   - Ⓒ Daydreams tell about things that are real.
   - Ⓓ No one can dance without a pair of magic shoes.

Talk about your answers to questions 1 and 2. Tell why you chose the answers you did.

PART THREE: Check Your Understanding

Remember: Some things you read are real, and some things are make-believe.

★ To figure out if what you are reading is mostly real, ask yourself, "Could all of the events really happen? Do the characters act as they might in real life?"

★ To figure out if what you are reading is mostly make-believe, ask yourself, "Are any of the events unlikely or magical? Do animals talk? Do characters do impossible things?"

Read this story about a boy who finds some new pets. As you read, ask yourself, "Which parts of the story are mostly real?" Then answer the questions.

Eddie's New Pets

Eddie went exploring in his backyard. He was searching for crickets. When he found two of them, he scooped them up and put them into a jar. He added some dirt, some leaves, and a small stick. He then put the lid on the jar and poked several holes in the top. Eddie then placed his new pets on a windowsill in his bedroom.

That night, as Eddie crawled into bed, he said good night to his crickets. "Good night," replied one of the crickets. Eddie blinked his eyes and looked closer into the jar. He saw a cricket knocking on the glass. "Will you set us free tomorrow?" asked the cricket. "Our parents are going to be worried about us."

3. Which of these could really happen?

Ⓐ Eddie's crickets ask to be freed.

Ⓑ Eddie puts two crickets into a jar.

Ⓒ Eddie sees a cricket knock on the side of the jar.

Ⓓ Eddie's cricket says "Good night."

4. You know that this story is mostly make-believe because

Ⓐ boys can't go exploring in their backyard.

Ⓑ no one places jars on a windowsill.

Ⓒ people do not say "good night" to their pets.

Ⓓ pets cannot talk to their owners.

Look at the answer choices for each question. Read why each answer choice is correct or not correct.

3. Which of these could really happen?

Ⓐ Eddie's crickets ask to be freed.

This answer is not correct because crickets cannot talk. This part of the story is make-believe. It could not really happen.

● Eddie puts two crickets into a jar.

This answer is correct because a boy could really put two crickets into a jar. This part of the story is real. It could really happen.

Ⓒ Eddie sees a cricket knock on the side of the jar.

This answer is not correct because crickets cannot knock. This part of the story is make-believe. It could not really happen.

Ⓓ Eddie's cricket says "Good night."

This answer is not correct because crickets cannot talk. This part of the story is make-believe. It could not really happen.

4. You know that this story is mostly make-believe because

Ⓐ boys can't go exploring in their backyard.

This answer is not correct because boys could really go exploring in their backyard.

Ⓑ no one places jars on a windowsill.

This answer is not correct because people could really place jars on a windowsill.

Ⓒ people do not say "good night" to their pets.

This answer is not correct because people could really say good night to their pets.

● pets cannot talk to their owners.

This answer is correct because pets cannot talk to their owners.

PART FOUR: Learn More About Distinguishing Between Real and Make-believe

★ Real stories include biographies, news reports, and informational articles.

★ Make-believe stories include fables, fairy tales, folktales, myths, legends, tall tales, and science fiction.

Read this letter written by one friend to another. Then answer the questions.

July 20, 2005

Dear Sarah,

How is your new house? Many things have changed in the neighborhood since you moved away.

My cat, Fluffy, hasn't been acting like himself lately. I think he misses you. I wish he could talk and tell me what's wrong.

The family that moved into your house seems strange. They don't come out of the house very often, and when they do, they never say hello. Their curtains are drawn all day. My brother says that maybe they're from outer space.

Last week, I couldn't even go to swim class because I was as sick as a dog! I am in level four now. I hope I reach level five before the end of the summer.

When can you come and visit? Write soon, and let me know.

Love,

Noriko

5. Which of these could really happen?

Ⓐ Sarah comes to visit Noriko.
Ⓑ The new neighbors come from Mars.
Ⓒ Noriko blinks her eyes, and Sarah appears.
Ⓓ Noriko's cat tells her what's wrong.

6. You can tell that the information in the letter is mostly real because

Ⓐ no one has new neighbors.
Ⓑ Noriko has a cat that talks.
Ⓒ the letter tells about things that could really happen.
Ⓓ people often act like dogs when they are sick.

7. Which of these could <u>not</u> really happen?

Ⓐ Noriko receives a letter from Sarah
Ⓑ Noriko becomes friends with the new neighbors.
Ⓒ Noriko is sick and turns into a dog.
Ⓓ Noriko reaches level five in her swim class.

8. Which of these could really happen?

Ⓐ A new family moves into Sarah's old house.
Ⓑ A new neighbor travels to outer space
Ⓒ Noriko's cat tells Sarah that he misses her.
Ⓓ Sarah's swim teacher is a fairy princess.

Read this journal entry. Then answer the questions.

April 3

Today our class took a field trip to the City Aquarium. There was so much to see!

We watched penguins and seals. They like to swim and show off for visitors. Then we went to see different kinds of reptiles, like snakes and lizards. We also saw lots of frogs. Some of the frogs live in places that are hot and wet. Their colors are very bright.

Next we went to the tide pool. We got to stick our hands in the clear salt water and hold creatures like crabs, starfish, and sea urchins. There was even a tiny horseshoe crab. The animals usually live in the ocean. I wonder if they miss their home.

We ended our visit with the Sea Lion Show. We saw two sea lions dancing across the stage waiting for a fish reward. Then they jumped in the water and did lots of tricks. Some people got wet. Our teacher got a sea lion kiss.

We sat outside and ate the lunches that we brought. Then it was time to go back to school. While we were on the bus, our teacher asked us what we liked best. We told her that it was hard to choose. We liked everything that we saw.

9. Which of these could really happen?

- Ⓐ Frogs live in places that are hot.
- Ⓑ Penguins take a field trip.
- Ⓒ Sea lions go to a dance.
- Ⓓ Crabs run away from the tide pool.

10. Which of these could <u>not</u> really happen?

- Ⓐ Sea lions eat fish.
- Ⓑ Sea lions kiss a teacher.
- Ⓒ Children live in a tide pool.
- Ⓓ Frogs have bright colors.

11. Which of these could really happen?

- Ⓐ Sea lions do lots of tricks.
- Ⓑ Crabs take a bus to the ocean.
- Ⓒ Starfish go to live in the sky.
- Ⓓ Sea lions teach children how to do tricks.

12. Which of these could <u>not</u> really happen?

- Ⓐ Children eat lunch outside.
- Ⓑ Seals sing and dance on the stage.
- Ⓒ Seals show off for visitors.
- Ⓓ Children get wet at the Sea Lion Show.

★ A test question about distinguishing between real and make-believe may ask you to tell the difference between things that could happen in real life and things that could not.

★ A test question about distinguishing between real and make-believe often contains the words *could really happen* or *could not really happen*.

Read this fable written by Aesop. Then answer questions about the fable. Choose the best answer for Numbers 13 and 14.

The Caged Bird and the Bat

A singing bird was confined in a cage, which hung outside a window. The bird had a way of singing at night when all other birds were asleep. One night, a bat came and clung to the bars of the cage. The bat asked the bird why she was silent all day and sang only at night.

"I have a very good reason for doing so," said the bird. "It was once when I was singing in the daytime that a man was attracted by my voice. So he set his nets for me and caught me. Since then, I have never sung except by night."

But the bat replied, "It is no use your doing that now when you are a prisoner. If only you had done so before you were caught, you might still be free."

Distinguishing Between Real and Make-believe

13. Which of these could really happen?

Ⓐ A man catches a bird.
Ⓑ A man turns into a bird.
Ⓒ A bird writes a song.
Ⓓ A bird teaches a bat to sing.

Distinguishing Between Real and Make-believe

14. Which of these could <u>not</u> really happen?

Ⓐ A bird lives in a cage.
Ⓑ A bat talks to a bird.
Ⓒ A bird stays silent all day.
Ⓓ A bat flies near a birdcage.

Read this fairy tale. Then answer questions about the fairy tale. Choose the best answer for Numbers 15 and 16.

The Frog Prince

Of all the toys the princess had, she loved her golden ball the most. One day, the ball bounced in a deep, dark well. The princess began to cry when she heard a deep voice say, "If I get your ball back, will you promise me something?" The princess looked up to see a frog. The princess said she would promise him anything if he got her ball back.

So the frog dove down and quickly came back up with the ball. "What do you want me to promise?" asked the happy princess.

"That you will let me live with you and be your friend," answered the frog.

"I'll have to think about that," said the princess. The frog could see that the princess didn't want to be his friend. So, tearfully, he said good-bye.

"Wait," said the princess. "Don't be sad. I'll be your friend." She picked him up and kissed him.

Suddenly, the frog was gone, and in his place stood a fine prince, who said, "Only the kiss of a kind-hearted princess could remove the spell that a witch put on me." The prince and the princess became good friends. One day, they decided to marry. And they lived happily ever after.

Distinguishing Between Real and Make-believe

15. Which of these could not really happen?

Ⓐ A ball bounces into a well.

Ⓑ A frog dives into a well.

Ⓒ A frog says a tearful good-bye.

Ⓓ A princess becomes friends with a prince.

Distinguishing Between Real and Make-believe

16. Which of these could really happen?

Ⓐ A frog talks to a princess.

Ⓑ A frog does a favor for a princess.

Ⓒ A witch turns a prince into a frog.

Ⓓ A princess cries when she loses her toy.

Strategies Ten–Twelve REVIEW

PART ONE: Read a Notice

Read this notice about a contest. Then answer questions about the notice. Choose the best answer for Numbers 1 through 6.

CALLING ALL YOUNG ARTISTS!

Do you like to draw or paint? Do you like animals? Would you like to do something to help animals? Then hop like a bunny and pick up a paintbrush. We need you to enter the Abram Wildlife Association's Calendar Contest.

Every year, the Abram Wildlife Association creates a calendar. We want next year's calendar to show your artwork. We will choose 12 winners from the drawings and paintings we receive. The winning artwork will appear in next year's calendar, "Young Artists Look at Animals." Send us your artwork, based on one of these themes.

- People Helping Animals
- Animal Babies
- Endangered Animals
- Troubled Habitats
- Wild Animals Are Not Pets

Your art could be the first step in saving the life of an endangered animal. Don't say you're too busy. Make time to help save the world's wild animals! Drop off your original artwork at Holden Public Library by May 1. Judging will take place on May 5. All winners will be notified by mail.

Identifying Author's Purpose

1. The author's purpose in paragraph 2 is to

Ⓐ explain what the contest is about.
Ⓑ entertain readers with a story about animals.
Ⓒ persuade readers to help animals.
Ⓓ describe the work of the Abram Wildlife Association.

Interpreting Figurative Language

4. Which of these is a simile?

Ⓐ hop like a bunny
Ⓑ you like to draw
Ⓒ you like animals
Ⓓ like to do something

Identifying Author's Purpose

2. What is the author's purpose in the last paragraph?

Ⓐ to inform readers how to enter the contest
Ⓑ to persuade readers to enter the contest
Ⓒ to describe a prize-winning poster
Ⓓ to entertain readers with silly animal stories

Distinguishing Between Real and Make-believe

5. Which of these could really happen?

Ⓐ A boy from the planet Venus wins the contest.
Ⓑ A dog draws a poster and sends it to the contest.
Ⓒ Every year, the Abram Wildlife Association creates a calendar.
Ⓓ One of the contest judges is a lion.

Interpreting Figurative Language

3. In the last paragraph, what do the words *make time* mean?

Ⓐ "look at one's watch"
Ⓑ "draw a clock"
Ⓒ "wait to do something"
Ⓓ "do something even if one is busy"

Distinguishing Between Real and Make-believe

6. Which of these could <u>not</u> really happen?

Ⓐ A tiger lives happily in an apartment.
Ⓑ Children help save wild animals.
Ⓒ Some wild animals are in danger.
Ⓓ Wild animals live in the United States.

PART TWO: Read an Article

Read this article about cats. Then answer questions about the article. Choose the best answer for Numbers 7 through 12.

The Care and Feeding of Your Pet Cat

Cats can be lots of fun, but they do need care. You need to make sure you will have enough time to feed, play with, and brush your cat every day. You will also need to spend time cleaning its litter box. Cats depend on their owners for everything. A cat owner is like a parent.

Some people think cats are unfriendly. They are not. Cats don't need lots of attention. Sometimes they seem unfriendly. But they are not. Cats are often loving and cuddly. When a cat wants to be cuddled, it will often jump in your lap. If it wants to be patted, it will rub your hand. Cats have a way of showing other feelings. If a cat's tail is straight up, it is excited that you're near. If a cat hisses, leave it alone. Sometimes cats need a time out.

You can feed your cat wet food or dry food. You can also mix them together. Just make sure the food is of good quality. Feed your cat two times a day. If you give your cat canned food, throw out any food that hasn't been eaten after half an hour. Never give your cat dog food. Also, never feed your cat chocolate, bones, or table scraps. Even milk products can make your cat ill.

Don't give your cat too many treats. Most treats contain lots of sugar and fat. They can really pack on the pounds. Older cats often have trouble with their weight. You don't want to add to the problem.

Your cat should have fresh, clean water available at all times. Change the bowl at least once or twice a day. On hot days, you might even want to add some ice to your cat's water.

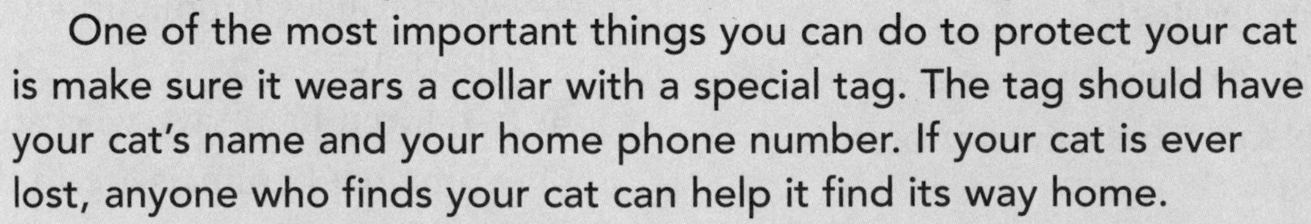

One of the most important things you can do to protect your cat is make sure it wears a collar with a special tag. The tag should have your cat's name and your home phone number. If your cat is ever lost, anyone who finds your cat can help it find its way home.

If you're ready to bring a cat into your home, remember that there are many of them ready to be adopted at animal shelters.

Identifying Author's Purpose

7. The author wrote the article mainly to
   - Ⓐ entertain readers with a funny animal story.
   - Ⓑ explain how to care for a pet cat.
   - Ⓒ persuade readers to go to adopt a cat.
   - Ⓓ describe the different ways cats behave.

Identifying Author's Purpose

8. You know your answer to question 7 is correct because the article mainly
   - Ⓐ tells an enjoyable story.
   - Ⓑ gives facts about something.
   - Ⓒ tries to convince readers to do something.
   - Ⓓ describes what kinds of food cats like to eat.

Interpreting Figurative Language

9. In the first paragraph, cat owners are compared to
   - Ⓐ cats.
   - Ⓑ parents.
   - Ⓒ pets.
   - Ⓓ children.

Interpreting Figurative Language

10. The words *pack on the pounds* mean
    - Ⓐ "come in large packages."
    - Ⓑ "contain lots of sugar."
    - Ⓒ "make your cat fat."
    - Ⓓ "make something worse."

Distinguishing Between Real and Make-believe

11. Which of these could really happen?
    - Ⓐ A cat hisses at a stranger.
    - Ⓑ A cat calls you when it is lost.
    - Ⓒ A cat uses a brush to groom itself.
    - Ⓓ A cat cleans its own litter box.

Distinguishing Between Real and Make-believe

12. Which of these could <u>not</u> really happen?
    - Ⓐ A cat holds its tail straight up.
    - Ⓑ A cat jumps into its owner's lap.
    - Ⓒ A cat gets its own food and water.
    - Ⓓ A cat likes both wet food and dry food.

Strategies One–Twelve FINAL REVIEW

PART ONE: Read a Folktale

Read this Native-American folktale. Then answer questions about the folktale. Choose the best answer for Numbers 1 through 12.

The First Medicine

Once upon a time, a very sick old man entered an Iroquois village. Over each wigwam, there was a sign. The sign told to which clan the owner of the wigwam belonged. A beaver skin meant that the owner was of the beaver clan. A deer skin meant that the owner was of the deer clan. The old man went to each wigwam asking for food and a place to sleep. But each time, he was sent away.

Finally, he came to a wigwam with a bear skin. A kind woman lived there. She let the man into her wigwam. The old man told the woman to go out and search for certain herbs. She prepared these herbs, following the old man's directions. The old man took the medicine and became better in no time.

A few days later, the old man came down with a fever. This time, he told the woman to search for different herbs. Again, this medicine healed him. This was repeated many times. Each time the old man became sick, the woman would gather different herbs, make a new medicine, and cure him.

At last, the old man told the woman that she now knew all the secrets for curing diseases. He told her to plant a hemlock tree in front of her wigwam. The tree would grow high in the air above all others. This would show that the bear clan ranks higher than all other clans.

Finding Main Idea

1. The folktale is mostly about

Ⓐ how a woman learned the secrets of medicine.

Ⓑ what the signs over Iroquois wigwams meant.

Ⓒ why there are so many hemlock trees.

Ⓓ how medicine is made from plants.

Recognizing Cause and Effect

4. What happened each time the old man became sick?

Ⓐ The woman went out to search for bears.

Ⓑ The people of the village turned him away.

Ⓒ He showed the woman how to make a new medicine.

Ⓓ The woman planted a hemlock tree in front of her wigwam.

Recalling Facts and Details

2. In the folktale, which of these animal skins was not found in the Iroquois village?

Ⓐ beaver

Ⓑ bear

Ⓒ coyote

Ⓓ deer

Comparing and Contrasting

5. How was the woman of the bear clan different from the other people in the village?

Ⓐ She did not turn the old man away.

Ⓑ She had more room in her wigwam.

Ⓒ She had an animal skin over her wigwam.

Ⓓ She knew the old man had the secret of medicine.

Understanding Sequence

3. Which of these happened last?

Ⓐ The old man went to each wigwam looking for food and a place to sleep.

Ⓑ A kind woman let the old man in.

Ⓒ The old man entered an Iroquois village.

Ⓓ The old man came down with a fever.

Making Predictions

6. The next time a sick old man enters the Iroquois village, the people will probably

Ⓐ run away from the village and hide.

Ⓑ order the woman to cure him.

Ⓒ send him away, as they did before.

Ⓓ try to help him as much as possible.

Finding Word Meaning in Context

7. The word *ranks* in the last paragraph means

Ⓐ "sings or makes a noise."
Ⓑ "has a position in a group."
Ⓒ "gives off a strong smell."
Ⓓ "lives in a certain place."

Drawing Conclusions and Making Inferences

8. From the folktale, you can tell that

Ⓐ the old man did not want to share his secrets with the woman.
Ⓑ wigwams were made from a variety of animal skins.
Ⓒ the old man shared his secrets with the woman because she was willing to help him.
Ⓓ all diseases can be cured with herbs.

Distinguishing Between Fact and Opinion

9. Which of these is a *fact*?

Ⓐ The deer clan is better than the bear clan.
Ⓑ The old man is very smart.
Ⓒ Most people in the village were selfish.
Ⓓ The woman followed the old man's directions.

Identifying Author's Purpose

10. The folktale was written in order to

Ⓐ describe what an Iroquois village looked like.
Ⓑ get readers to learn more about the Iroquois.
Ⓒ explain why the bear clan has a high place among the Iroquois.
Ⓓ entertain readers with a story that tells about the first medicines.

Interpreting Figurative Language

11. In the folktale, the words *in no time* mean

Ⓐ "quickly."
Ⓑ "never."
Ⓒ "slowly."
Ⓓ "quietly."

Distinguishing Between Real and Make-believe

12. Which of these could <u>not</u> really happen?

Ⓐ A sick old man enters an Iroquois village.
Ⓑ A bear gathers herbs to make medicine.
Ⓒ A kind woman lets an old man into her wigwam.
Ⓓ A hemlock tree grows to be very tall.

PART TWO: Read an Article

Read this article about how Jewish people arrived in America. Then answer questions about the article. Choose the best answer for Numbers 13 through 24.

We all know that Christopher Columbus sailed across the Atlantic in 1492. The story of his trip has been retold many times.

Do you remember King Ferdinand and Queen Isabella from the story of Columbus? They were the king and queen of Spain. They gave Columbus the money he needed to make his trip. The king and queen were not always so generous, though.

In the same year that Columbus set sail, the king and queen passed a new law. They made up their mind that they did not want Jewish people living in their country. The new law forced all Jews to leave Spain at once.

Some Jewish families went to live in Portugal. Later, some of these families settled in South America. As years passed, however, Jews living in South America were also told to leave.

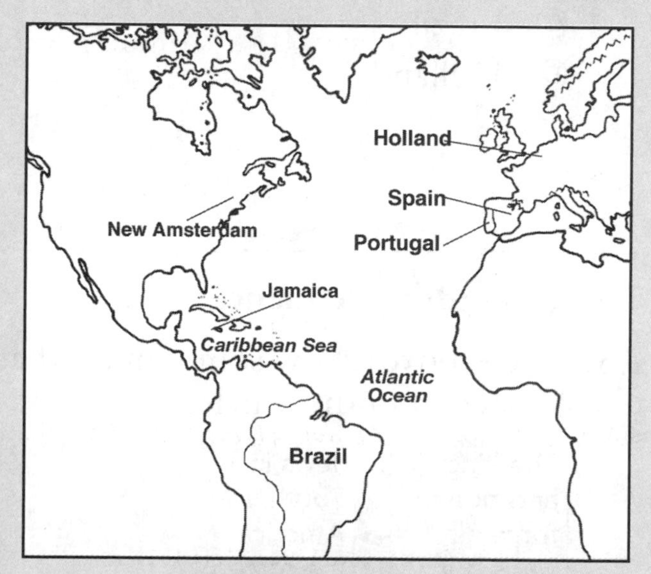

In 1645, a group of Jews living in Brazil decided to go to Holland. As their ship sailed through the Caribbean Sea, a storm caused them to stop in Jamaica. While they waited there, they ran out of money. They were not able to pay for the long trip to Holland. Instead, they set sail on a ship headed to New Amsterdam, a Dutch colony.

One day in September 1645, their ship landed in New Amsterdam. Today we know New Amsterdam as New York City. That day, 23 Jewish passengers stepped off the boat and into history. The history of Jewish people in the United States began with their arrival.

Finding Main Idea

13. The best title for the article is

Ⓐ "1492: An Important Year."

Ⓑ "The Dutch Colony of New Amsterdam."

Ⓒ "The Journey of Christopher Columbus."

Ⓓ "How Jewish People Came to the United States."

Recalling Facts and Details

14. When a storm forced them to stop in Jamaica, the Jews had been sailing to

Ⓐ Spain.

Ⓑ Portugal.

Ⓒ Brazil.

Ⓓ Holland.

Understanding Sequence

15. These boxes show some things that happened in the article.

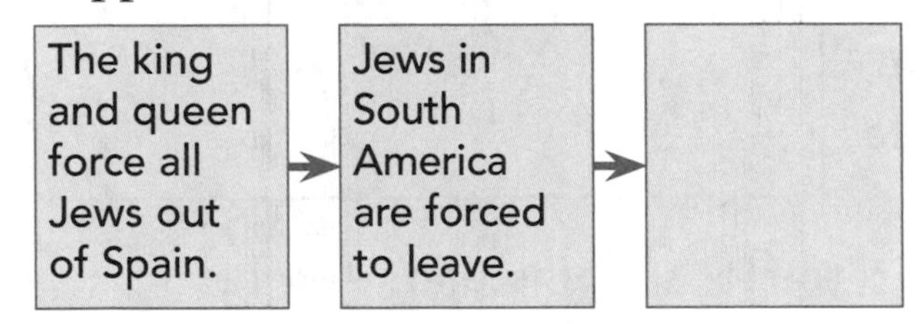

What belongs in the empty box?

Ⓐ Jewish passengers arrive in New Amsterdam.

Ⓑ The king and queen pass a new law.

Ⓒ Some Jews leave Portugal for Brazil.

Ⓓ Columbus sailed across the Atlantic.

Recognizing Cause and Effect

16. The Jews did not go to Holland because

Ⓐ they weren't allowed there.

Ⓑ there was a storm in the Caribbean Sea.

Ⓒ the king and queen would not let them.

Ⓓ they thought New Amsterdam would be a better place to live.

Comparing and Contrasting

17. How were Brazil and Spain alike?

Ⓐ Both countries have the same laws.

Ⓑ The people of both countries spoke the same language.

Ⓒ Both countries told Jewish people to leave.

Ⓓ Both countries are ruled by kings and queens.

Making Predictions

18. What probably happened to the Jewish people who came to New Amsterdam?

Ⓐ They soon left to return to Brazil.

Ⓑ A new law was passed that forced them to leave.

Ⓒ They stayed and were later joined by other Jewish families.

Ⓓ They returned to Spain after the king and queen no longer ruled.

Finding Word Meaning in Context

19. In paragraph 2, the word *generous* means

Ⓐ "fond of all people."
Ⓑ "happy to help others."
Ⓒ "unkind to others."
Ⓓ "fair in all things."

Drawing Conclusions and Making Inferences

20. From the article, you can figure out that

Ⓐ the king and queen passed a new law in 1492.
Ⓑ the people of Brazil welcomed the Jews.
Ⓒ life in Portugal was difficult for the Jews.
Ⓓ most people did not obey the new law passed by the king and queen of Spain.

Distinguishing Between Fact and Opinion

21. Which of these is an *opinion*?

Ⓐ Columbus sailed across the Atlantic in 1492.
Ⓑ Twenty-three Jews arrived in New Amsterdam in 1645.
Ⓒ What happened to the Jews in Spain was terrible.
Ⓓ After the Jews were forced out of Spain, they settled in different places.

Identifying Author's Purpose

22. The author's purpose in paragraph 2 is to

Ⓐ describe the country of Spain.
Ⓑ get readers to feel sorry for the Spanish Jews.
Ⓒ entertain readers with a tale about Columbus.
Ⓓ explain something about the king and queen of Spain.

Interpreting Figurative Language

23. In paragraph 3, the phrase *made up their mind* means

Ⓐ "passed a law."
Ⓑ "acted unfairly."
Ⓒ "made a mistake."
Ⓓ "made a decision."

Distinguishing Between Real and Make-believe

24. Which of these could not really happen?

Ⓐ Jewish people were forced to leave their homes.
Ⓑ The king and queen of Spain didn't want Jewish people living in Spain.
Ⓒ There was a big storm in the Caribbean Sea.
Ⓓ The Jewish families watched television on their way to New Amsterdam.

PART THREE: Read a Story

Read this story about a young boy named Nick. Then answer questions about the story. Choose the best answer for Numbers 25 through 36.

And So He Came

In school we learned about immigrants. Immigrants are people who leave one country to live in another. A large number of immigrants came to live in America during the early 1900s.

When I got home from school, I asked my mom if anyone from our family was an immigrant. She reached up high on the book shelf and took out a photo album. It was filled with black and white pictures of people in her family. She showed me a picture of her grandfather. She told me how her grandfather had to escape from the country where he was born. A war was going on and there was a lot of fighting.

"Is he my great-grandfather?" I asked.

"Yes, he is," Mom answered. I smiled.

My great-grandfather boarded a ship and traveled across the Atlantic Ocean to America. The ship landed at Ellis Island in New York. Everyone got off the boat and waited inside a big building. Doctors there made sure my great-grandfather was healthy. If he wasn't, he might have had to go back to his country. His name was written in a book that lists the name of each person who passed through Ellis Island. The book also shows their answers to certain questions. Two of these questions were "How much money do you have?" and "Where are you going to live?"

My great-grandfather came here alone. He didn't know one person. Other people came as families. Some family members weren't allowed to stay. They were sick. The family had to decide then and there if they were going to split up or go back to their homeland together.

My great-grandfather was given the okay to stay in the United States. He stayed in New York City the rest of his life. He worked in a bakery for a while. Then he married my great-grandmother. She worked in a factory. She was a seamstress who made dresses. Later my great-grandfather became a police officer. He died long ago, before I was born. I wish I had known my great-grandfather. He must have been very brave. I would have enjoyed hearing him tell me all about his life.

Finding Main Idea

25. What is the story mostly about?

Ⓐ a man who comes to the United States from another country

Ⓑ a boy who learns about his great-grandfather

Ⓒ an island in New York called Ellis Island

Ⓓ the many people who came to America in the early 1900s

Recalling Facts and Details

26. Nick's great-grandfather came to the United States because

Ⓐ there was a war going on in his country.

Ⓑ he had no money.

Ⓒ he had no family.

Ⓓ he needed a doctor.

Understanding Sequence

27. Which of these happened first to Nick's great-grandfather?

Ⓐ He got married.

Ⓑ He became a police officer.

Ⓒ He arrived at Ellis Island.

Ⓓ He was checked by doctors at Ellis Island.

Recognizing Cause and Effect

28. If doctors found people at Ellis Island to be sick, they might have to

Ⓐ stay at Ellis Island.

Ⓑ return home.

Ⓒ stay with their family.

Ⓓ go to the hospital.

Comparing and Contrasting

29. A seamstress is most like a

Ⓐ baker.

Ⓑ doctor.

Ⓒ police officer.

Ⓓ dressmaker.

Making Predictions

30. Which of these is Nick most likely to do next?

Ⓐ Write a letter to his great-grandfather.

Ⓑ Become a police officer.

Ⓒ Read a book about New York.

Ⓓ Find out more about people who came through Ellis Island.

Finding Word Meaning in Context

31. You can tell that an *immigrant* is someone who

Ⓐ lived in New York long ago.
Ⓑ travels from one country to live in another.
Ⓒ is a passenger in a ship.
Ⓓ lived during the early 1900s.

Drawing Conclusions and Making Inferences

32. You can tell from the story that Nick

Ⓐ has never been to New York City.
Ⓑ never got to meet his great-grandfather.
Ⓒ works hard in school.
Ⓓ enjoys learning about other countries.

Distinguishing Between Fact and Opinion

33. Which of these tells what someone thinks or feels?

Ⓐ Other people came as families.
Ⓑ He must have been very brave.
Ⓒ My great-grandfather came here alone.
Ⓓ In school we learned about people who came to the United States long ago.

Identifying Author's Purpose

34. The story was written in order to

Ⓐ describe.
Ⓑ explain.
Ⓒ persuade.
Ⓓ entertain.

Interpreting Figurative Language

35. In paragraph 6, the words *then and there* mean

Ⓐ "right away."
Ⓑ "in front of others."
Ⓒ "after a while."
Ⓓ "over and over again."

Distinguishing Between Real and Make-believe

36. Which of these could <u>not</u> really happen?

Ⓐ A man travels alone.
Ⓑ A family comes to the United States.
Ⓒ A boy goes back in time to visit his great-grandfather.
Ⓓ A doctor checks to see if someone is healthy.

PART FOUR: Read a Story

Read this story about a girl named Victoria. Then answer questions about the story. Choose the best answer for Numbers 37 through 48.

Right-Handed or Left-Handed?

Victoria arrived in class panicked. She couldn't find her report that she had worked so hard on. And she was supposed to present her report to the class today. A knot tightened in Victoria's stomach. What could she do? She had already searched her backpack three times. She walked nervously over to her teacher. She hoped he wouldn't be upset.

Victoria explained her problem to Mr. Forrest. "I must have left my report on my desk at home," she said. Mr. Forrest understood. He told Victoria that she could present her report the next day. Victoria breathed a sigh of relief. He wasn't upset after all. Mr. Forrest then told Victoria that she would need to at least talk to the class today about the subject of her report.

Victoria stood at the front of the class and began. "I have always wondered why some people are left-handed and others are right-handed. I think this is the most fascinating subject to learn about. I am left-handed. Only ten people out of one hundred are left-handed like me. We live in a 'right-handed' world. Most tools are made for right-handed people. I have learned that there are many reasons some people use their left hand and others use their right."

"The brain has two sides, the left side and the right side. The right side of the brain helps the left side of the body. The left side of the brain helps the right side of the body. For most people, the left side of the brain is the strongest half. This is why the right side of the body is better able to do things. Most people write, read, and speak using the left side of their brain. This is different for people who are left-handed. The right side of their brain is stronger. The left side of the body is better able to do things. That is why they write using their left hand."

Victoria ended her talk by asking the question, "How many of you are left-handed, besides me?" There are twenty other students in Victoria's class. Only one raised a hand.

Finding Main Idea

37. The story mainly tells
- Ⓐ why a girl forgot her homework.
- Ⓑ how to become left-handed.
- Ⓒ why some people are left-handed.
- Ⓓ where a girl left her report.

Recognizing Cause and Effect

40. Victoria breathed a sigh of relief because
- Ⓐ she was still going to get to speak in front of the class.
- Ⓑ the students enjoyed her report.
- Ⓒ her teacher was not upset.
- Ⓓ she found her report in her backpack.

Recalling Facts and Details

38. Mr. Forrest can be described as
- Ⓐ harsh.
- Ⓑ understanding.
- Ⓒ thoughtful.
- Ⓓ uncaring.

Comparing and Contrasting

41. A problem is most like a
- Ⓐ result.
- Ⓑ difficulty.
- Ⓒ solution.
- Ⓓ disaster.

Understanding Sequence

39. The boxes show some things that happened in the story.

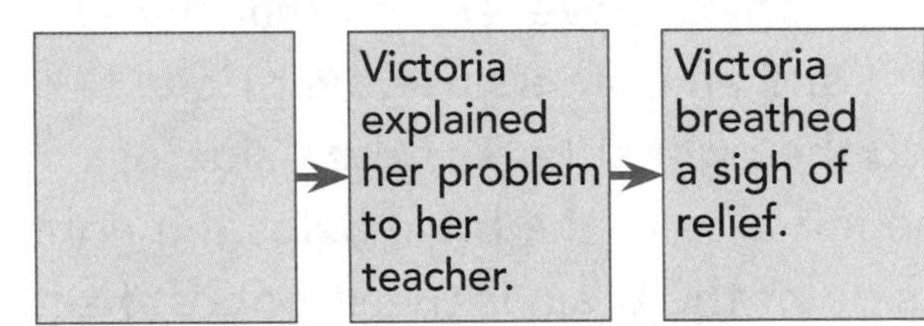

What belongs in the empty box?
- Ⓐ Victoria asked how many of her classmates were left-handed.
- Ⓑ Victoria explained that the brain has two sides.
- Ⓒ Victoria stood in front of the class and began her talk.
- Ⓓ Victoria felt a knot tighten in her stomach.

Making Predictions

42. Suppose you are in a room filled with forty people. Predict how many would be left-handed.
- Ⓐ 4
- Ⓑ 6
- Ⓒ 12
- Ⓓ 14

Finding Word Meaning in Context

43. In the story, *panicked* means

Ⓐ "tired."

Ⓑ "surprised."

Ⓒ "confused."

Ⓓ "nervous."

Drawing Conclusions and Making Inferences

44. There is enough information in the story to figure out that

Ⓐ Victoria will not need to bring her report into class after all.

Ⓑ most of the students in Victoria's class are right-handed.

Ⓒ the left side of Victoria's brain is stronger than the right.

Ⓓ Victoria will receive a high grade on her report.

Distinguishing Between Fact and Opinion

45. Which of these tells what someone thinks or feels?

Ⓐ "I am left-handed."

Ⓑ "I must have left my report on my desk at home."

Ⓒ "The brain has two sides, the left side and the right side."

Ⓓ "I think this is the most fascinating subject to learn about."

Identifying Author's Purpose

46. The story was written in order to

Ⓐ describe how a girl felt about giving a report.

Ⓑ explain facts about why some people are left-handed.

Ⓒ entertain readers with a funny story.

Ⓓ persuade readers to learn more about why they are either left-handed or right-handed.

Interpreting Figurative Language

47. The story says that a *knot tightened in Victoria's stomach.* This means that Victoria was

Ⓐ "worried."

Ⓑ "hungry."

Ⓒ "excited."

Ⓓ "ill."

Distinguishing Between Real and Make-believe

48. Which of these could really happen?

Ⓐ A girl is neither left-handed nor right-handed.

Ⓑ A class of twenty students is all left-handed.

Ⓒ A report suddenly appears in a girl's backpack.

Ⓓ A girls speaks in front of her class.